The Radio Amateur's Guide to EMC

Robin Page-Jones, CEng, MIEE, G3JWI

Radio Society Of Great Britain

Published by the Radio Society of Great Britain, Cranborne Road, Potters Bar, Herts EN6 3JE.

First published 1992

ISBN 1 872309 16 X

Cover design: Geoff Korten Design.
Illustrations: Derek Cole, Radio Society of Great Britain.
Production and typography: Ray Eckersley, Seven Stars Publishing.

Printed in Great Britain by Galliard (Printers) Ltd, Great Yarmouth.

Contents

Acknowledgements

Thanks are due to the many friends whose ideas and suggestions have contributed to this volume, and particularly the current members of the EMC Committee:

Bob Peace, G8SOZ
Norman Harper, G3ZCV
David Lauder, G1OSC
Fred Robins, G3GVM
Megan Smith, G0MEG

Special thanks to David Lauder, G1OSC, for making available the report of his work on the characterisation of filters and chokes which forms Appendix 3. Also to Hilary Claytonsmith, G4JKS, for her contribution to many discussions on style and content, and for her assistance in checking and revising the manuscript.

Robin Page-Jones, G3JWI

Chapter 1

Introduction

It is said, on very good authority, that the well-known work of reference *The Hitch Hiker's Guide To the Galaxy* has the words 'DON'T PANIC' in large friendly letters on the cover. This is advice which could well be on the cover of any EMC manual for, though it is unlikely that an EMC investigator would be faced with quite such trying situations as Mr Arthur Dent (or be quite so ill equipped to deal with them), there is no doubt that the EMC world is full of strange and unexpected effects, not to mention some fairly odd people. This, of course, includes a number of radio amateurs.

EMC is not a thoroughbred subject – more a rather ugly mongrel, being the product of bits and pieces from several engineering disciplines, some of which are extremely difficult mathematically. Like many mongrels it has a certain charm when you get to know it, but the question is how do you get to know it? Over the years an extensive body of knowledge on dealing with interference problems has grown up, but in many instances the explanation of why a particular solution works (or in some cases does not) is not clear. In addition to this, technical advance is so rapid that new problems are appearing all the time. In this manual the aim is to discuss the underlying causes rather than just listing standard remedies, so that the subject becomes an interest in its own right. The idea is to give the reader an insight into what EMC is all about, so that whatever problems turn up in the future, they may be tackled, if not with confidence, at least without trepidation.

The approach is always down to earth, and explanations and analogies are used instead of maths. This has been done for two reasons. The ostensible reason is that the mechanism of most interference problems is so complicated, and plagued by unknown factors, that mathematical analysis is unrewarding – to say the least. Underlying this is the far more important reason that many people do not find mathematical explanations very interesting or convincing. If you are the sort of person who feels that the world would be a better place if all sines were swinging outside country pubs, you will have no difficulty browsing through these pages. For anyone who wishes to follow up a topic in more depth, references are given at the end of each section.

If there is one thing that is characteristic of the last decade of the twentieth century, it is that we have all come to realise that the world is finite, and co-operation, or at least tolerance, is the name of the game. It could be said that, in their own field, radio amateurs have always been aware of this, and band plans and codes of practice have existed from the earliest days. True, one does hear complaints of rude or thoughtless behaviour, but this in itself is an indication of how deeply the idea of good practice is ingrained.

'EMC' is such a widely used abbreviation that we tend to forget that it stands for ELECTROMAGNETIC COMPATIBILITY, and it is the compatibility which is the thing that matters. Many people in the computer and entertainment electronics fields, both amateur and professional, have only a very limited knowledge of how this compatibility can be achieved, and it has to be said that, despite the efforts of national societies and of the amateur radio press in general, many amateurs are not really conversant with what is good practice in any particular circumstance.

This manual has been produced with the intention of fulfilling two purposes. The first is to assist radio amateurs to avoid EMC problems by practising good radio housekeeping, and to diagnose and cure any problems which do occur. The second is to provide background material which will be relevant to everyone who has an interest in the subject.

EMC is a worldwide problem and, with a few exceptions, the information contained in this book is relevant to any country. In this regard it will be noticed that the internationally accepted word 'antenna' is used instead of 'aerial', even when discussing domestic radio and TV. British readers may object that everyone in the UK says 'TV aerial' – whatever the officially approved usage may be. However, after much thought, it has been decided to use 'antenna' throughout, and it is hoped that British readers will accept the need for uniformity.

The text is divided up into eight chapters, covering the main areas of interest. So far as possible each chapter is complete in itself, and cross-referencing is used only to show where more information on a particular subject can be found. This inevitably involves some repetition, but this is not necessarily a disadvantage, in that it gives a slightly different perspective on the underlying problems, depending on the theme of the particular chapter. Where appropriate, a summary is provided at the end of the chapter to give 'immediate action' information. In an emergency, it should be possible to use the summary to look up what to do, without reading the main part of that chapter. This is where the 'DON'T PANIC' comes in! To avoid the main chapters being cluttered by too much detail, a number of specific problems which are not relevant to the technical discussion in any particular

section have been placed in Chapter 9, 'Some Specific EMC Problems'.

Solving an EMC problem can be a pleasure; it doesn't have to be tackled in an atmosphere of gloom. After all, many people enjoy doing crossword puzzles; why not enjoy solving EMC problems? In some ways they can be similar – though it has to be admitted that it is unusual for a crossword to come knocking at your door demanding to be solved! However, like it or not, EMC has become an almost inevitable feature of amateur radio, so when trouble does come to your door, reach confidently for this book and, above all, DON'T PANIC.

Chapter 2

Radiation – wanted and unwanted

The one thing that links together all radio enthusiasts, young and old, amateur and professional, is electromagnetic radiation. The ability to communicate without any apparent medium has a fascination of its own which never entirely fades, however jaded one may become with the nuts and bolts of radio and electronics.

Natural radio-frequency radiation has been around for a very long time. In fact, if the cosmic background radiation really is the remnant of the 'big bang', as current theories suggest, then radio signals have a direct link to the creation of the universe; a good pedigree by any standard. RF radiation is only a small part of the electromagnetic spectrum, which extends from very low frequency radio waves right up to gamma rays which have wavelengths of only about 10^{-14} metres. Visible light is a fairly thin slice somewhere near the middle, with wavelengths in the region of half a micron (0.5µm) (Fig 2.1).

Visible light, very roughly, forms the division between non-ionising radiations like radio waves and ionising radiations such as x-rays and gamma rays. Ionising radiations, as their name implies, are energetic enough to have a direct affect on the atomic structure of certain materials, and if this material happens to be a living cell serious damage can be done. Non-ionising radiation, on the other hand, only causes atoms and molecules to vibrate (without coming apart), giving rise to heating effects. The sunlight which gets through to the earth includes both features in a more-or-less optimum mix for sustaining life. As wavelengths get longer, the waves get less energetic, and it is generally agreed that at radio frequencies the only significant effect is heating [1, 2]. What radiation really is, and how it fits into life, the universe and everything, is a fascinating

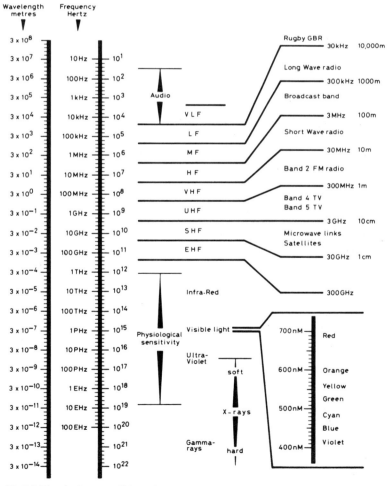

Fig 2.1. The electromagnetic spectrum

3

subject, and anyone interested should read one of the many popular books on the background to modern physics. We shall, however, confine ourselves to the uses and abuses of radio frequencies.

What is RF radiation?

So far as radio frequencies are concerned, radiation is caused by accelerating electric charges, which in electric circuit terms means a varying current in some sort of conductor. A current flow implies both electric and magnetic fields, and it is the interaction of these two fields which gives rise to electromagnetic radiation. Many academic textbooks which deal with antennas and radiation offer an impressive display of advanced mathematics, but not much from which the plain man can form a mental picture of what is actually going on. At the other end of the scale, excessively simplified explanations can give a false impression of understanding. The truth of the matter, of course, is that there is no simple picture of the mechanism of radiation, and the best that can be done is to try to get some sort of feel for what is going on, coupled with an appreciation of the magnitude of the effects which are of interest in amateur radio in general, and to EMC problems in particular.

Power density and field strength

These two parameters turn up regularly in EMC literature, and most importantly in the new EMC standards for domestic and industrial equipment. These new standards set down limits for the immunity to RF fields, and also the limits of permissible radiated interference, for all types of equipment. It is therefore essential that everyone in the radio and electronics world should be at least on nodding terms with them. The relationship between power density and field strength embodies most of what the average man in the street (with an EMC problem) needs to know about radiation, and is nicely illustrated by the following technical day dream.

Power density

Imagine a large sphere somewhere out in space, made of magic glass with exactly the same electrical properties as space itself. At the centre of the sphere is a transmitting antenna which is truly isotropic, so that it radiates equally in all directions. Further imagine the surface of the sphere is divided up into squares of one metre side, like the panes of glass in a huge spherical greenhouse (Fig 2.2(a)). The power density in watts/square metre is simply the fraction of the power which passes through each square. For instance, assuming that the power of the transmitter is 100W and the radius of the sphere is 282m, so that there are a million squares (the surface area of a sphere is $4\pi R^2$), then the power density would be $100\mu W$/square metre.

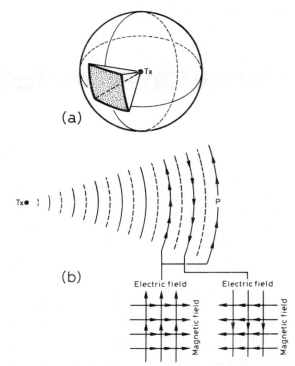

Fig 2.2. (a) Radiation falling on one square on surface of imaginary sphere. (b) Fields seen by an observer located at point P on the surface of the sphere

Impedance of free space

Now imagine that the sheets of glass are replaced by sheets of conductive material, rather like the conductive foam used for packing CMOS integrated circuits, but having a resistivity of exactly 377Ω per metre square. The foam will absorb all the radiated power and none will be left over, so that the situation, as seen by the transmitter, is indistinguishable from the magic glass condition, ie the radiation seems to be passing out into space. This is analogous to an infinitely long transmission line which, from the transmission end, appears to be terminated in its characteristic impedance, but which can be terminated in its characteristic impedance anywhere along its length, without changing what the transmitter sees.

Field strength

For this we have to imagine that we are back in the magic greenhouse, and that all the conductive foam has been cleared away. Think of just one of those metre squares of magic glass, and assume that the polarisation of the radiation is such that the electric field is lined up across the square, and the magnetic field is up and down, like the divisions on a sheet of graph paper (Fig 2.2(b)). If we could take a magic voltmeter and measure the voltage across the sides of the square, this would be the field strength in volts per metre. Since this voltage is across the characteristic impedance of free space, which is 377Ω, we can relate this to the power density by the simple power-voltage-resistance formula

$$P = V^2/R \quad \text{or} \quad V = \sqrt{(PR)}$$

For our 100W transmitter 282m away, the power density is 100μW/square metre, so the field strength is

$$\sqrt{(100 \times 10^{-6} \times 377)} = 194\text{mV}$$

across one metre of space or 194mV/m.

There is an approximate way of working out the field strength if we know the power radiated and the distance away, and that is by taking the square root of the power, multiplying by 5.5, and then dividing by the range in metres.

In our case,

$$\frac{5.5 \times \sqrt{100}}{282} = 195\text{mV/m}$$

At this point it is essential to emphasise that it is not practical to use these simple formulas to predict with any accuracy the conditions in the neighbourhood of an amateur antenna. The most obvious thing that comes to mind is that practical antennas are not isotropic, but this is the least of our troubles since a correction can always be made for whichever antenna we are using. The really serious problem is that amateur antennas are usually fairly close to earth and also surrounded by other obstructions, so the field strength at any point is really the sum of direct and reflected waves. This means that the field strength can vary from zero to at least twice the calculated value, depending on the phase of the received waves. Another problem, which is particularly relevant to EMC investigations, is that at lower frequencies the receiving point is often too close to the source for the calculated figures to have any meaning. All in all, though the calculated figures must be treated with the greatest circumspection, they can be useful in giving an idea of where problems are likely to arise.

Near and far fields

While on the subject of definitions, it is a good time to bring up two more which are important to the understanding of EMC problems. These are 'near field' and 'far field'. The near field exists relatively close to the antenna, where the relationship between the inductance and capacitance of the antenna itself, and the fields surrounding it, is the same as it would be in or around actual components; energy flows backwards and forwards between antenna and field (Fig 2.3). In some ways the effect is similar to the space charge around the cathode of a valve, where there is a balance between electrons emitted and those falling back to the cathode. Any conductors, such as

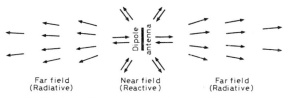

Fig 2.3. The flow of RF energy around a short dipole antenna

mains cables or TV antennas, in the near-field region will be coupled to the radiating antenna by direct capacitive or inductive coupling, and this can give rise to much larger unwanted coupling than might be expected.

The far field, often called the 'radiation field', is the region well away from the source, where the magnetic and electric fields are on their own, and proceed through space at right-angles to one another and to the direction of propagation. Under these conditions the intensities of the two fields are in phase so that, going back to our magic sphere, an observer sitting at a point P (Fig 2.2(b)) on the surface of the sphere would see the electric and magnetic fields sweeping over him out into space. As the fields pass him they increase and decrease, in phase with one another, following the RF cycle. In the far field the electric and magnetic fields cannot exist independently; destroy one and the other disappears as well.

How far from the source does the near field extend? Like so many questions about radiation there is no simple answer. As a rough guide, it can be said that for a half-wave dipole the near and far fields are equal in intensity at a distance of about one-fifth of a wavelength. Inside that distance the near field predominates, but as the distance increases the near field rapidly declines, becoming negligible at a distance of a few wavelengths. At lower frequencies, 3.5MHz for instance, the influence of the near field spreads out quite a long way, and may well encompass the home of the amateur and those of his near neighbours as well.

Signal pick-up and capture area

Signal pick-up on a wire which is in a radiated field depends on a number of factors, and the situation can be very complicated. The various effects can be illustrated by looking at a simple case; that of a half-wave dipole placed parallel to the electric field. Energy is extracted from an area around the dipole which depends only on the wavelength and is approximately 0.13 times the wavelength squared ($0.13\lambda^2$ square metres). This is known as the 'capture area' of the antenna. If the dipole is correctly matched by connecting a resistor of 75Ω across the terminals, then the total power extracted is the capture area multiplied by the power density. Interestingly, the capture area of a dipole, which is much shorter than a half-wave, is almost the same as that of the full-size half-wave

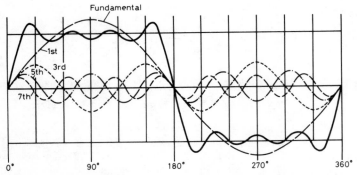

Fig 2.4. A square wave can be analysed into a sine wave plus odd harmonics

dipole, provided that it is tuned to resonance and correctly matched by some form of antenna tuning unit (ATU). The trade-off is that the bandwidth of the antenna system becomes very narrow as the antenna is made shorter, and losses in the ATU become prohibitive.

Only half of the available power actually appears in the load. The other half is lost in the radiation resistance of the dipole, which is just another way of saying that half the power extracted from the field is re-radiated. Where the load resistance is smaller than the radiation resistance, a larger proportion of the energy is re-radiated and vice versa. In practice this means that almost any wire will have a resonance at some frequency or other, and will re-radiate energy if a nearby transmitter happens to be on or near that frequency. This brings near-field conditions into places where they would not otherwise be expected, and is responsible for many of the unpredictable effects which bedevil the investigation of interference problems.

Unwanted radiation

Though the principles underlying all forms of RF radiation are the same, there are two quite different aspects which impact on the whole of the radio and electronic world. One is the deliberate radiation of signals from an antenna, where the object is to radiate as much of the energy supplied by the transmitter as possible. Despite the vagaries of imperfect grounds and cluttered gardens, this is a comparatively controlled situation. The other aspect is quite the reverse. This is where unwanted signals are accidentally radiated from some form of equipment which is supposed to be carrying out some completely non-radio function. In the majority of such cases the details of the actual process of radiation is exceedingly complex, involving a large number of unknown variables, so that it is almost always easier to consider the problem as a whole than to attempt detailed analysis. It is perhaps a paradox that the computer, which on the face of

it is the symbol of the strictly logical approach, is, under its business-like exterior, a seething mass of unpredictable radiation sources.

Generally speaking, this type of radiation takes place where current is rapidly changing, usually in some form of switched circuit. Nowadays the most common source of interference is from switched electronic circuits such as in computers and games machines. The amount of energy depends on the current involved and the speed of switching and usually these are related; faster logic devices tend to draw more current. It is a well-known fact that pulses of current can be analysed into a series of harmonically related sine waves, and that the steeper the sides of the pulse, the higher the harmonics involved (Fig 2.4).

Even quite modest home computers can involve pulses with edges of only a few nanoseconds (a nanosecond is one thousandth of a microsecond), giving harmonics up to tens or even hundreds of megahertz. Because there are so many pulse streams, all with their associated harmonics, the net result is RF energy radiated over a wide spectrum, with peaks at various clock frequencies and their harmonics. Interfering signals usually leak out of the offending equipment by a complicated mixture of conduction and radiation. Input and output leads, particularly the mains supply, can act as transmission lines, carrying the signals a considerable distance before the energy is lost in radiation or other losses.

There is a general rule that antennas which are good for transmission will also be good for reception, and this is just as true when applied to the unwanted radiators involved in equipment which accidentally generate interference. Practically, this means that those computers and similar devices which allow interference to leak out will also be susceptible to disturbances getting in. In some instances the disturbance can be due to a genuine RF signal from a legitimate transmitter such as one of the public services or amateur radio, but in most cases the source is a switching transient caused by something being switched on or off nearby – often a fridge or electric power tool. Of course the fridge or tool should be suppressed, but then so should the computer; ideally both should be suppressed to the appropriate level.

References

[1] 'RF hazards and the radio amateur', R P Blackwell and I F White, *Radio Communication* February 1982.
[2] *Microwave Handbook*, M H Dixon (ed), Vol 2, RSGB, Chapter 11.

Chapter 3

Good radio housekeeping

The phrase 'good radio housekeeping' has been coined to cover all the factors which contribute to trouble-free amateur radio operation. The phrase may be new but the ideas are a distillation of conventional wisdom, which has been accumulated over decades of amateur activities. Throughout the 'fifties and 'sixties, the main problem facing amateurs was interference to VHF TV caused by harmonics from HF transmitters. This problem has diminished over the years, partly because transmitter design has improved, but mainly because of the demise of VHF TV in many countries including Britain. In recent years, interference caused by the fundamental transmission getting into all types of electronic equipment has become the major problem.

The term 'breakthrough' is normally used to describe this phenomenon, emphasising the fact that it is really a shortcoming on the part of the equipment being interfered with, and not a transmitter fault. This is not to say, of course, that the avoidance of problems from faulty or inadequate transmitters is not important; on the contrary, it is too big a subject to include as part of this general housekeeping section, and is dealt with in Chapters 4 and 6.

Minimising breakthrough

The main object of good radio housekeeping is to minimise breakthrough to local domestic entertainment equipment, by arranging for as much of the precious RF energy as possible to go where it is wanted – in the direction of the distant station – and as little as possible into the local surroundings where, if you are lucky, it gets lost. If you're unlucky it ends up as breakthrough in your neighbour's TV or video. In many cases it can be rightly argued that the immunity of the domestic equipment is woefully inadequate, but that does not absolve the amateur from the responsibility of keeping his RF transmissions under reasonable control. Many of the features which contribute to minimising breakthrough also help in reducing received interference so, while the virtue of good neighbourliness is undoubtedly its own reward, there is the added bonus of better all-round station performance.

The new regulations

Until recently the only regulations which most UK amateurs were aware of were those incorporated in their licence. So far as breakthrough is concerned, the concept of 'undue interference' was used which gave scope for wide interpretation. The official view was usually favourable to the amateur, provided it could be shown that the problem was not due to defects in his equipment.

During the last few years, two important factors have influenced events. One is the veritable explosion of electronic entertainment and computer equipment in the home, coupled with (or perhaps causing) a more commercial approach to solving EMC problems by the authorities. The other is the increasing amount of EMC legislation, and particularly so far as the UK amateur is concerned, the harmonisation of standards within the European Community (EC).

It could be said that it is not really necessary for amateurs to concern themselves with the new regulations, since they are likely to be advised of any important changes of practice, either through their licences or through the publications of their national societies. On the other hand, knowledge of the standards is invaluable in assessing what is reasonable and what is not, when considering EMC problems. As a compromise, a few notes are given here to show what the standards are all about, and to point anyone who wants to go further in the right direction.

Generally speaking, the various national standards are based on recommendations from an international body known as 'Comité International Spécial des Perturbations Radioélectrique' – almost always abbreviated to 'CISPR' – so there is a a good deal of similarity between them despite differing national requirements and attitudes. In the UK, EMC standards are published by the British Standards Institute (BSI), and these are harmonised to EC standards, which are officially known as 'European Norms'. Some standards, called 'generic standards', cover a whole range of equipment, while others cover specific types of equipment. Inevitably, sometimes the subject of the specific standard also falls into the general scope of the generic standard. When this happens the specific standard always takes precedence. All this has led to an apparent tangle of standards and numbers, but things are not really as complicated as they appear, and the point to remember is that the BS standard is the UK version of the EC standard, so that from the amateur's point of view there are only a few important documents.

Anyone wanting specific information should always consult the standards themselves since, apart from any other consideration, they are updated from time to time. Copies of the BS standards are held in the reference sections of some of the larger public libraries and can be consulted on request. Though at first sight the standards seem rather formidable, they are not too hard going for the ordinary interested person. As with most such documents, the secret is not to try to read it straight through from beginning to end, but to pick out the key parts first. In our case this will probably be levels and limits. When these have been digested, read the clauses which relate to them. When you have got an idea of what it's all about, read through the whole document to make sure that nothing has been missed.

The immunity standards
These standards lay down the level of unwanted signal – amateur, CB, public service or other radio source – that a particular piece of equipment must be able to withstand and still function properly.

(a) For radio and TV receivers and associated equipment, BS 905 Part 2 (European Norm EN 55 020). This is a fairly complicated document but the main point is that the relevant equipment must be capable of operating satisfactorily in reasonable RF field strengths. More significantly from the amateur point of view, there is also a requirement for immunity to signals on external leads such as the braid of the antenna coaxial cable, the mains input and the speaker leads.
(b) For other types of electronic equipment such as burglar alarms, washing machines and pretty well anything with active electronic components in it, except ITE, the generic standard is EN 50 082-1. Again the equipment is required to operate in reasonable RF fields.
(c) ITE (information technology equipment), which for most practical purposes means computers and their associated communications links, has an immunity standard of its own – EN 55 101-3; this is similar to EN 50 082-1.

The emitted interference standards
These are the standards which lay down the limits of interference which may be emitted by any piece of equipment. There are several standards covering different types of interference-generating equipment.

(a) For ITE, BS 6527 (EN 55 022). This deals with computers and related equipment, and lays down the maximum permissible levels of interference that may be generated.
(b) For household appliances, BS 800 (EN 55 014). This covers interference from household equipment containing motors, thermostats, and semiconductor control circuits, and includes domestic power tools.
(c) For interference from radio and TV sets, BS 905 Part 1 (EN 55 013).

In a brief summary such as this, it is not practical to quote levels; so much depends on the frequency band and how the measurements are made. It is clear, however, that even when all equipment in neighbours' houses is up to the new standards, there will still be a problem where small signals are being received, as is the case in amateur radio. This is to be expected since the emission regulations are framed around broadcast reception, where signals are usually very large by amateur standards.

What this all comes down to is that while the new regulations will at least define the limits which will prevent intolerable interference conditions, it is going to be good radio housekeeping which will determine whether practical amateur radio activity is possible in any particular location.

Antennas
By far the most important factor in preventing both breakthrough and received interference problems is the antenna and its siting. It is unfortunate that most of us live in small houses with small gardens and neighbours in close proximity; well-sited antennas are likely to be unpopular just where they are most needed. The basic requirement is to site the antenna as high as you can, and as far as possible from your own house and from neighbouring houses. If there is any choice to be made in this regard give your neighbours the benefit of the increased distance – it is usually much easier to deal with any problems in your own home. It is a sad fact that many amateurs are persuaded by social pressures into using low, poorly sited antennas, only to find that breakthrough problems sour the local relations far more than fears of obtrusive antennas would have done.

HF antennas
The question of which antenna to use is a perennial topic and the last thing that anyone would want to do is to discourage experimentation, but there is no doubt that certain types of antenna are more likely to cause breakthrough than others. It is simply a question of horses for courses; what you can get away with in a large garden or on HF Field Day may well be unsuitable for a confined city situation. In conditions where EMC is of prime importance, the antenna system should be:

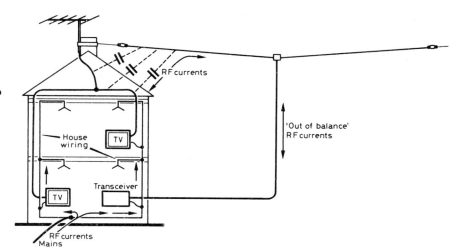

Fig 3.1. Capacitive coupling to house wiring, TV feeder etc

(a) *Horizontally polarised.* TV down leads and other household wiring tend to look like an earthed vertical antenna so far as HF radio waves are concerned, and are more susceptible to vertically polarised radiation.

(b) *Balanced.* This avoids out-of-balance currents in feeders giving rise to radiation which has a large vertically polarised component. Generally, end-fed antennas are unsatisfactory from the EMC point of view and are best kept for portable and low-power operation.

(c) *Compact.* So that neither end comes close to the house and consequently to TV down leads and mains wiring. Antennas to be careful with are the extended types such as the W3DZZ trap dipole or the G5RV because, almost inevitably, in restricted situations one end is close to the house.

Fig 3.1 shows how capacitive coupling to the house wiring can occur with a dipole antenna. What the house wiring actually sees is electric charges rushing towards it and away from it in the antenna. This causes similar charges to flow in the house wiring to maintain equilibrium. These charges are, of course, RF currents which can find their way into anything connected to the wiring.

The effective capacitance between two parallel wires is greater than one might expect from application of the 'parallel plate' capacitance formula, because 'fringe' effects become dominant, and the lines of force tend to spread out as in Fig 3.2. The capacitance between two wires 1m long and 2m apart is in the order of a few picofarads. (It is perhaps worth a slight digression to point out that any wire has a capacitance in its own right, and in this case the lines of force can be considered as travelling outwards into space seeking another conductor which may be infinitely far away. A plate at the end of the universe, perhaps!). When the distance of the antenna from the house is considerably greater than the dimensions

of the antenna itself, then there is not a large difference between the distance from various parts of the antenna to the house wiring, so that direct coupling from different parts of the antenna tends to cancel out. (At any given time some parts of the antenna will be at positive potential, while other parts are equally negative). These effects can be interpreted in terms of the near and far fields of antennas of different physical size, but doing so would not really shed any light on the issue.

On frequencies of 14MHz upwards it is not too difficult to arrange an antenna fulfilling these requirements, even in quite a small garden. A half-wave dipole or small beam up as high as possible and 15m or more from the house is the sort of thing to aim for. The simple multiple dipole arrangement shown in Fig 3.3 is a popular low-cost solution. The inverted-V configuration is not ideal but, provided that the angle between any pair of elements is kept as large as possible, it makes a very practical compromise.

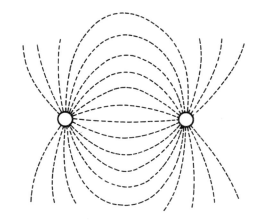

Fig 3.2. Lines of force between two conductors

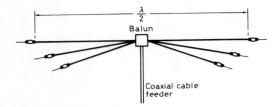

Fig 3.3. Multiple dipoles. Each pair of elements is approximately λ/2 for the band required

At lower frequencies compromise becomes inevitable, and most of us will have no choice but to have one end of the antenna near the house, or to go for a loaded vertical antenna which can be mounted further away but which has the inherent disadvantage of being vertical. A small loop antenna is another possibility, but in general any antenna which is very small compared to a wavelength will have a narrow bandwidth and a relatively low efficiency. Many stations use a G5RV or W3DZZ trap dipole for the lower frequencies, but have separate dipoles (or a beam if they are lucky) for the higher frequencies, sited as far down the garden as possible.

VHF antennas

These follow the same general rules as for HF antennas, except that, because of the relatively high frequencies involved, it is much easier to get the antenna a few wavelengths away from the house. The big problem with VHF is that large beams can cause very high field strengths. For instance, 100W fed to an isotropic transmitting antenna in free space would give a field strength of about 3.6V/m at a distance of 15m. The same transmitter fed into a beam with a gain of 20dB would give a field strength, in the direction of the beam, of 36V/m at the same distance. Again, it comes down to the fact that if you want to run high power to a high-gain beam, the antenna must be kept as far from neighbouring houses as possible and, of course, as high as practical.

Operation in adverse situations

The obvious question arises as to what to do if your garden is small or non-existent, or domestic conditions make a simple wire tuned against ground the only possibility. First of all, and most important, don't get discouraged and go off the air altogether. Many amateurs operate very well from amazingly unpromising locations. It is really a question of cutting your coat according to your cloth. If there is no choice but to have antennas very close to the house, or even in the loft, then it will almost certainly be necessary to restrict the transmitted power, in conjunction with a consideration of the modes to be used. Not all modes are equally 'EMC friendly', and it is worth looking at some of the more frequently used modes from this point of view.

(a) *SSB*. This is the most popular mode, and most operators use it at least some of the time. Unfortunately it is also the least EMC friendly, particularly where audio breakthrough is concerned.

(b) *FM*. This is a very EMC friendly mode, mainly because in most cases the susceptible equipment sees only a constant carrier turned on and off every minute or so. This is why FM is used for CB radio in many countries. Unfortunately it is not a practical mode for HF, except for the special case of FM on the 28MHz band.

(c) *CW*. This is the old faithful for those with EMC problems, because it has two very big advantages. First, providing the keying waveform is well shaped with rise and fall times of about 10ms or so, the rectified carrier is not such a problem to audio equipment as SSB. The slow rise and fall gives relatively soft clicks which are often accepted by neighbours when SSB would not be. The second advantage is that it is possible to use lower power for a given contact. As any QRP enthusiast will testify, it is possible to have satisfactory CW contacts on a few watts, though amateurs with EMC problems usually compromise by running about 20W, and turning the power up outside problem hours or to give a quick call in difficult situations. Of course, low-power CW is not everybody's cup of tea, but it does provide a way of staying on the air, even in the most difficult circumstances.

(d) *Data*. Generally the data modes used by amateurs are based on frequency-shift keying (FSK), and should be EMC friendly. All data systems involve the carrier being keyed on and off – when going from receive to transmit and vice versa – and consideration should be given to the the carrier rise and fall times, just as in CW.

Earths

The provision of an adequate earth has occupied the attention of radio enthusiasts since the earliest days. When the wavelengths in use were long, as they invariably were in those days, the earth formed a vital part of the radiating system, as it does today in medium-wave and long-wave broadcasting stations. In amateur operation the antenna tuned against ground is still used for the 1.8 and 3.5MHz bands, though its use at higher frequencies has declined mainly due to its poor EMC performance. With this type of antenna the RF current actually flows in and out of the ground connection, and it is the difficulty of keeping this current out of the mains supply which is one of its most serious drawbacks. A similar situation exists with out-of-balance currents in a nominally balanced antenna system.

The classic way of isolating the RF earth from the

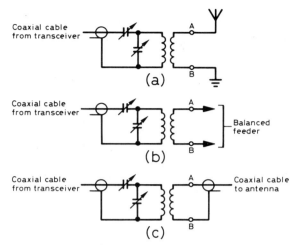

Fig 3.4. Inductively coupled ATU (Z-match) isolates RF from mains earth

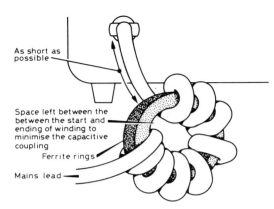

Fig 3.5. Ferrite ring choke on transceiver mains lead

mains earth is by using an inductively coupled ATU, such as the 'Z match' as shown in Fig 3.4. Configuration (a) is for end-fed antennas, and (c) is suitable for either an unbalanced antenna, such as a ground plane, or for a balanced antenna which is fed with coaxial cable, with a balun at the antenna end. Configuration (b) is the usual way of feeding balanced line – either low-impedance or open-wire feeder – and requires no comment, except perhaps to remind users of the risk of static charge build-up since the antenna can be completely earth-free.

Sometimes it is suggested that the mains earth should be disconnected from the transceiver, but this is a danger-ous practice since the mains earth is there for the express purpose of preventing electric shock in the event of an equipment fault. A far better plan is to isolate RF from the mains by using ferrite ring chokes as in Fig 3.5. If the cable is inconveniently thick, fewer turns on a stack of four or five cores can be used. The object is to make the number of cores in the stack multiplied by the square of the number of turns be about 400. Where the station comprises not only the transceiver but also mains-pow-ered ancillary units, then the ferrite choke should be in the common mains feed to all the units.

Usually the whole mains lead is wound on the cores, but it is possible to choke the mains earth lead separately. If this is done, make sure that the standard of workman-ship is adequate and the conductor is of sufficient rating to comply with the safety requirements. If there is any doubt about safety aspects, the current IEE Wiring Regu-lations should be consulted. The best way to find these is by enquiring at your local library.

The most practical RF earth consists of several copper pipes, at least 1.5m long and preferably longer, spaced at least 1m apart, and driven into the ground so that the tops are just clear of the surface. The pipes should be joined together with the heaviest copper wire available. The connection to the ATU/transceiver should be as short as possible and of as thick wire as possible. Bear in mind that the RF earth is in parallel with unwanted earth paths – particularly the mains wiring – and the object is to provide a low-impedance path down which the majority of the earth currents will flow. To this end, flat copper strip or heavy-duty braid can be used to advantage. Where the shack is located in an upstairs room, the earth connection will inevitably be long and in many cases it is doubtful if an earth connection is of any benefit. Since the earth will be carrying RF currents, it will radiate and could cause problems in downstairs rooms. Where the earth lead is a resonant length, very undesirable effects can occur, mak-ing the rig much 'hotter' to RF than would otherwise be the case. With an upstairs shack, it is especially important

---

WARNING
Protective multiple earthing (PME)

Some houses, particularly those built or wired since the middle 'seventies, are wired on what is known as the 'PME system'. In this system the mains earth of the house wiring is bonded to the neutral where the supply enters the building. In the event of certain rare fault conditions it is possible for the earth and neutral conductors all over the house to rise to a voltage significantly above that of the true earth (ie the earth out in the garden). In extreme cases the earth neutral voltage could be the full mains voltage above true earth. For this reason the supply authorities advise certain precautions regarding the bond-ing of metal work inside the house.

WHERE A HOUSE IS WIRED ON THE PME SYS-TEM, DO NOT CONNECT ANY EXTERNAL (ie radio) EARTHS TO APPARATUS INSIDE THE HOUSE unless suitable precautions are taken.

Appendix 1 gives further details of PME, and suggests possible procedures.

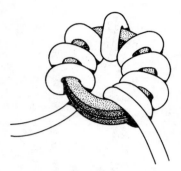

Fig 3.6. Ferrite ring choke on coaxial feeder

to avoid arrangements which use the earth as part of the antenna system. In other words, go for a balanced antenna or, if an unbalanced antenna is the only possibility, use a coaxial feeder system which has the earth (or better still the counterpoise or ground plane) as far from the house as possible. Where coaxial feeder is used, the connection to the ATU/transceiver should be as in Fig 3.4(c).

One possible consequence of poor antenna/earth policy is that RF energy can enter the transceiver through its ancillaries and their connecting leads. Pick-up in the microphone cable is well known, but electronic keyers and other control equipment are also vulnerable. Where a transceiver is operated from an external power supply, it is not uncommon for RF to find its way into the stabilising circuits of the supply, causing erratic operation which is sometimes mistaken for a transceiver fault. Mild cases can be treated as cases of breakthrough, using ferrite chokes and bypass capacitors as appropriate, but the real answer is to examine the antenna/earth arrangements and the station layout to eliminate the problem at source.

Feeders

At VHF the choice of feeder is limited to the selection of a suitable coaxial cable. On HF several options are available, and each has its merits and disadvantages. These are discussed at length in the appropriate handbooks [1, 2], but from the EMC point of view the simplest solution is to use coaxial cable with a suitable balun at the antenna end to achieve a balanced feed. Baluns are not difficult to make and suitable designs will be found in references [3], [4] and [5].

Where the domestic situation permits, the feeder should be buried, preferably in a protective plastic pipe (a coating of wax floor polish will help to prevent moisture from penetrating the PVC sheath). If possible, the outer of the coaxial cable should be earthed before it enters the house. Where RF currents occur on the outer of the cable, they can be eliminated, or at least reduced, by using a ferrite-ring choke, as in Fig 3.6. If twin feeders are to be used, pay particular attention to maintaining the balance of the antenna, and ensure that the individual wires of the twin feeder are always much closer to each other than they are to other conducting objects. In all cases feeders should fall away as nearly as possible at right-angles to the antenna (Fig 3.7).

Lightning protection is outside the scope of this manual, but the provision of suitable earths for this purpose is obviously an essential part of any antenna/feeder system. Further information will be found in references [1], [2] and [4].

Passive intermodulation products (PIPs)

This phenomenon has been familiar to generations of radio operators, both amateur and professional, as the 'rusty bolt effect'. In recent years, the proliferation of complex public service radio systems with co-located transmitters and receivers has brought it into a new prominence, and it has now achieved, not only a proper title, but also the ultimate mark of technical respectability – a three-letter abbreviation.

All mixing and harmonic generating circuits use non-linear elements such as diodes to distort the current

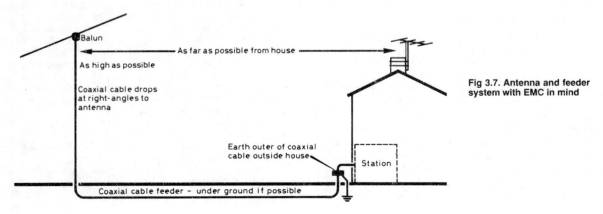

Fig 3.7. Antenna and feeder system with EMC in mind

waveform, and hence to generate the required frequency components. A similar effect will be produced whenever the naturally produced semiconductor layer in a corroded metal joint forms an unwanted diode. These unwanted diodes are usually most troublesome in the antenna system itself, particularly in corroded coaxial cable connectors. In the case of a single transmitter, the effect simply causes excessive harmonic radiation, but where two or more transmitters are operating in close proximity the result can be quite spectacular intermodulation product generation. On receive, the result is much-reduced receiver intermodulation performance, manifesting itself by rather watery signals with strange, mixed-up modulation appearing where they have no right to be. In severe cases there will be a noticeably high noise floor, consisting of a mishmash of unwanted signals.

The best way to avoid troubles of this sort is to keep the antenna system in good repair and to examine all connections every few months. Now and then the 'rusty bolt effect' occurs in corroded metal gutters and similar structures not directly associated with the antenna system, but normally this will only be troublesome when high RF fields are involved.

References

[1] *Radio Communication Handbook*, RSGB.
[2] *ARRL Antenna Handbook*, ARRL.
[3] 'The ferrite-cored balun transformer', R G Titterington, *Radio Communication* March 1982.
[4] *HF Antennas for All Locations*, L A Moxon, RSGB.
[5] *Transmission Line Transformers*, J Sevick, ARRL.

SUMMARY – GOOD RADIO HOUSEKEEPING CHECKLIST

HF antennas

To minimise breakthrough, antennas should be:

(a) horizontally polarised;

(b) balanced – use a balun if appropriate;

(c) sited as far from your own and neighbouring houses as practical, and as high as possible;

(d) compact, to minimise direct coupling to house wiring etc;

(e) arranged so that the feeder drops vertically down to ground level. If coaxial feeder is used, run it underground (if possible) and earth the screen outside the house.

VHF antennas

These should be mounted as far from house wiring as possible. Particularly bear in mind the very high field strengths which can occur when high power is fed to high-gain beams.

Earths

(a) If at all possible, avoid arrangements which involve the earth as part of the antenna system, eg end-fed antennas tuned against ground.

(b) Isolate the RF earth from the mains earth by using an inductively coupled ATU.

(c) Make the mains earth as high an impedance as possible to RF by using a ferrite ring choke on the transmitter mains lead.

(d) Make the RF earth of as low impedance as possible. Use several copper pipes driven well into the ground, and connect to the station using as thick wire as practical; if possible, use copper strip or heavy-duty braid.

(e) Where the station is located upstairs, an RF earth may not be of any benefit and may cause trouble due to resonance effects. If a good RF earth is impossible, the best solution is to avoid the need for one by using a well-balanced antenna system.

Passive intermodulation products (the 'rusty bolt effect')

(a) Keep all antenna metalwork in good condition, making sure that all bolts are tight and joints free of corrosion. If galvanised iron wire guys are used, make sure that they do not form rusted contacts with the mast or tower.

(b) Check all RF connectors every few months and replace any that show signs of corrosion.

(c) Avoid siting antennas close to rusted gutters or similar structures.

Chapter 4

The EMC detective

For over a century one of the most popular forms of literature has been the detective story, and a glance at any bookstall will show no evidence of a reduction in the fictional crime rate. To many crime story enthusiasts, the most intriguing period is that of the classic amateur detectives, with their idiosyncratic methods and their convenient friends in high places. The one thing which immediately strikes the reader of these works is the strange fact that these characters have the knack of attracting crimes. Their very presence is sufficient to cause murder and mayhem to descend on their unfortunate neighbours.

The EMC detective is in a similar position in that problems literally come to his door. Almost certainly, though, it will not be a beautiful young lady who has found an (unwanted) body in her bath; it is much more likely to be a disturbed neighbour who is having trouble with his TV and suspects you of being the culprit. Anyone who operates an amateur station is almost bound to come up against a problem sooner or later, so willing or not, they will find themselves involved in a 'case'.

So, what approach should the EMC detective use when trouble does come to his door? First and foremost it should be realised that most EMC problems are complex, involving the interplay of a number of factors. There is nothing special about this; it is true of most accidentally occurring situations. Familiarity with computers has given many young electronic and radio enthusiasts the false impression that every technical problem can be broken down to a series of simple logical steps. This is an excellent approach where circumstances permit, but in the real world most 'non-engineered' situations involve a large number of unknown factors. EMC problems fall into this category, and it is impractical to tackle them by reference to a simple list of cures which can be applied without further thought. What is needed is a careful look at all the conditions involved before coming to any decision about causes and remedies.

In this section, the aim is to investigate interference (apparently) caused by amateur transmitters. Remedies are mentioned only in so far as they are part of the diagnostic process. Further information on remedies will be found in the appropriate chapters.

The preliminary investigation

Things usually start with a complaint from a neighbour about interference to some piece of domestic equipment – most likely a TV or hi-fi, though in recent years electronic telephones have become strong contenders in the interference league. In fact, RF radiation can affect any electronically controlled device, so it pays to keep an open mind at this stage, however bizarre the complaint may seem. The first thing to find out is if it really is your station that is causing the trouble. If your neighbour has been keeping a record of dates and times – as recommended in the RSGB's pamphlet *Neighbours' Questions Answered* [1] – then reference to the station log will tell you what you need to know. Assuming it is you, the next step is to determine whether it is due to spurious radiations from your transmitter or to inadequate immunity in your neighbour's equipment. The way this is tackled depends on what test gear is available – if you have a spectrum analyser or a suitable measuring receiver the job will be greatly simplified, but for the moment let us assume that only the resources of a typical amateur station are to hand.

Ask yourself the following questions:

1. Is the neighbour's equipment some form of radio device, such as a TV or radio receiver, which is suffering interference on specific frequencies?
2. If so, is similar equipment tuned to the same frequencies in your own house or at other neighbours' houses affected?

If the answer to both questions is 'yes', then it is probable that the interference is being caused by some form of unwanted radiation from your transmitter.

If the answer to both questions is 'no', then the chances are that the problem is due to breakthrough, ie insufficient immunity in the neighbours' equipment.

By far the commonest cause of breakthrough is pick-up by susceptible equipment of radiation from the antenna system of the amateur station, but it is worth checking that there is no RF energy leaking out of the transmitter itself. Run the transmitter into a dummy load, using the mode which normally gives the worst interference. If the interference is still evident when operating into the dummy load, then energy is leaking out of the transmitter itself, possibly directly through the case, but more likely via the mains lead. In either case the transmitter should be investigated along the lines discussed in Chapter 6. If the trouble is only present when the station is operating normally into the antenna system then a typical breakthrough problem exists.

Investigating a case of breakthrough

The first step is to try to get some idea of how severe the problem is. The easiest way to do this is to reduce the transmitter power while an assistant checks how the interference is affected. A couple of CB radios make a useful link which can be used by almost anyone, and greatly widen the field when looking for a willing assistant. If the breakthrough is significantly reduced when the transmitter power is reduced to about 50W PEP, then the problem can be classed as 'moderate''. If the interference still persists at powers down to about 10W it definitely falls into the 'severe' category. Make test transmissions on all the bands and modes available to you. It is worth trying all the modes and frequencies that you can use, even if you do not normally use them – everything is grist for the EMC detective's mill. During this preliminary phase of the investigation, find out if other neighbours are having trouble, and if so, under what circumstances. This obviously requires discretion, otherwise you will put ideas into peoples' heads and end up being blamed for every radio disturbance in the district. It is a reasonable assumption that you will already know if you have problems in your own home, but it is worth rechecking everything to see if any useful background information can be gleaned.

IF and intermodulation breakthrough

In addition to direct pick-up, radio and TV sets can suffer from more subtle forms of breakthrough. These fall into four categories:

1. *Direct intermediate-frequency (IF) breakthrough*, where the IF of some piece of radio equipment falls in or near an amateur band. The most common example is a transmission on the 10MHz band getting into the 10.7MHz IF of a VHF receiver. This is breakthrough caused by insufficient IF rejection in the receiver.
2. *IF breakthrough caused by harmonics of the amateur transmitter being picked up in the receiver IF*, for example the second harmonic of the 18MHz band entering the IF of a TV set. (The standard TV IF includes 36MHz.) A less likely possibility is the third harmonic of 3.5MHz entering the 10.7MHz IF of a VHF receiver. Cases of this sort indicate that the transmitter is radiating too much harmonic energy – it is no excuse to say that the susceptible receiver should be better designed.
3. *Image interference*. This where a signal on the 'wrong side' of the local oscillator beats with it to give the IF. It is fairly common on the 1.8MHz band, where amateur signals give image responses on medium-wave receivers. For instance, a receiver with a 455kHz IF tuned to 990kHz (303m) would have a local oscillator of 1,445kHz. This would beat with a strong amateur signal on 1.9MHz, which would be tuned in on the medium-wave band like any other signal. This is a case of breakthrough, caused by poor image rejection of the susceptible receiver.
4. *Amateur signals intermodulating with the harmonics of the local oscillator or other oscillators in the susceptible equipment, causing spurious responses.* These give rise to interference which is tuneable at the receiver, but is nevertheless a case of breakthrough.

At strategic points in the story the fictional detective reviews the situation, discussing the evidence with his or her somewhat dim assistant. Presumably the main reason for this is to prevent the reader from completely losing the thread of the plot, but in the case of the EMC detective the need to look carefully at the overall picture before rushing into action is essential to avoid having to keep calling on neighbours and trying things over and over again. This inevitably leads to loss of confidence, and allows any goodwill that may have existed at first to trickle away.

Looking for the evidence

The methods employed are applicable to all types of susceptible electronic devices, from music centres to burglar alarms, the only difference being in the route the RF energy takes to enter the equipment. In general, wherever external leads are connected to a unit there is a risk of RF pick-up causing trouble. As in all electrical circuits, the RF current must flow between two points of different potential; usually a crude wire antenna and a capacitance to earth. Hopefully, if the equipment designer has done a good job, these currents will have already been dealt with but, if not, then breakthrough problems are likely to occur. These can only be eliminated by identifying the vulnerable leads and increasing their effective impedance to radio frequencies by suitable chokes or filters, or by improving the bypassing of RF currents to earth, as discussed in Chapter 5.

It is a reasonable assumption that a wire which is very small compared to a wavelength will not pick up significant amounts of RF. For instance, in a case of HF breakthrough to a TV/video installation a few tens of

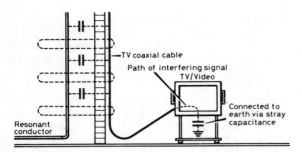

Fig 4.1. Energy coupled into TV antenna lead from resonant conductor

metres away from the transmitting antenna, it is unlikely that the signal will get in through the TV antenna itself. It is much more likely to be picked up on the braid of the coaxial feeder, or to be getting in through the mains or through some ancillary connection. The first thought is that the installation must have poor immunity, but before jumping to any conclusions check that there is no evidence of abnormally high signal pick-up caused by the local environment. This could be due to re-radiation from a resonant conductor in the vicinity, or to transmission-line effects causing excessive coupling into the TV antenna feeder, the mains lead or external speakers etc.

A crude transmission line can be formed between almost any conductor which is long (and roughly horizontal) and earth. In effect the fields are confined between the conductor and its image in the earth. This transmission line – if such a hotchpotch of unknowns can honestly be called a 'transmission line' – can pick up signals either directly, due to a remote section of the conductor being coupled to a source of RF energy, or by a resonance effect in the transmission line, which is bound to be mismatched.

Figs 4.1 and 4.2 are somewhat idealised illustrations of resonance and transmission-line effects, though in reality the difference between them is nothing like so clear cut. They are contributory factors in many cases of breakthrough, showing themselves by the fact that interference

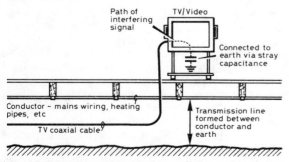

Fig 4.2. Interference entering TV through transmission-line coupling to the antenna lead

is worse on one band, and is noticeably affected by moving the equipment or its leads.

The best way to confirm a resonance of this type is to move round the area with a portable receiver tuned to the transmitter frequency and to note if a marked increase in signal strength occurs anywhere. To avoid overloading the receiver, the transmitted power should be reduced until the received signal is less than about S9.

Where a piece of equipment has ancillary items connected to it as part of the installation, eg a music centre with separate speakers, then the leads and ancillaries can form a loaded antenna which may resonate on an amateur frequency (Fig 4.3).

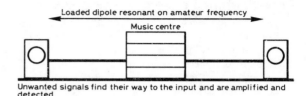

Fig 4.3. Speaker leads act as loaded dipole

A similar effect occurs when the TV or radio antenna coaxial feeder and all the metalwork of the antenna installation are resonant on an amateur frequency. Because of the end loading, the physical length may not give an accurate guide to the resonant frequency. The simplest way to confirm the existence of this type of problem is to disconnect the suspect lead or, where this is not possible, break up the resonance by wrapping the suspect lead onto a ferrite ring to form a lossy choke. If a ring is not practical, a ferrite rod salvaged from an old AM radio can be used. If this gives a significant change in the breakthrough then you are on the right lines. Don't forget, though, that there may be more than one mode of ingress, and several breakthrough signals may be adding or subtracting, so that the effect of any diagnostic activity may not be clear cut. Any change in the interference, even an increase, is an important clue.

When you have acquired all the evidence that you are likely to get, the only course is to proceed with the appropriate remedies which will be found in Chapter 5. Inevitably there will still be an element of trial and error but, by this stage, it should have been reduced to manageable proportions.

Are you completely innocent?

When there are several complaints of interference from different neighbours and a variety of equipment is affected, eg TV/video, audio, control circuits etc, the immediate thought must be that there is excessive coupling from the transmitting antenna to local electrical wiring. Have a good look at your station set-up – are you really practising good radio housekeeping? Go through the 'good radio housekeeping checklist' at the end of Chapter 3 or, better still, read the whole section and then go through the checklist! If the spirit of this section is being followed and the breakthrough is still severe, check to see if there is an unwanted resonance on feeders or earth lead – particularly if you are using an upstairs shack. Are antennas close to mains supply cables, or to telephone lines which may be acting as transmission lines for the RF? In most cases a rigorous application of good housekeeping will clear up the majority of the complaints, leaving a few which will by now have been reduced to the 'moderate' category, and can be dealt with as individual cases of breakthrough.

The misguided enthusiast

Occasionally one comes up against an isolated case of severe breakthrough where the complainant is an electronic entertainment enthusiast, and has piped his TV, video, music centre and his computer all over the house. Very often the installer has more enthusiasm than technical knowledge, so with a bit of luck he may be having trouble from sources other than yourself and be glad of a bit of advice. Look out for badly made coaxial feeder connections, long straggling leads and coaxial cables branching off to different destinations without proper splitter units. Often such cables are left unterminated when not in use, causing unwanted resonant circuits. One of the commonest defects of such installations is the use of unsuitable TV amplifiers which have very little selectivity and poor intermodulation performance. It is worth remembering that when the new EMC regulations come in to force, all such devices sold in the European Community will have to have a minimum immunity standard and carry the 'CE' mark. Unfortunately amplifiers purchased before then will still be around for a long time, but the existence of a standard will at least help to convince your neighbour that it is he who has the problem.

When your neighbour has put his own house in order, any remaining breakthrough problems can be considered individually and the appropriate remedies applied along the lines indicated in Chapter 5.

Investigating the suspect transmitter

If the answer to the original two questions:

1. Is the neighbour's equipment some form of radio device, such as a TV or radio receiver, which is suffering interference on specific frequencies?
2. If so, is similar equipment tuned to the same frequencies in your own house or at other neighbours' houses affected?

was 'yes', it is likely that the amateur station is radiating an unwanted signal which is interfering with anything using that frequency. By its very nature, this type of

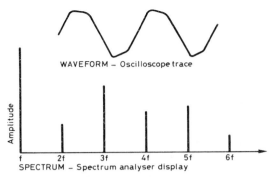

Fig 4.4. Typical harmonic content of a distorted sine wave

interference almost always involves some form of radio receiver, though it will not necessarily be a broadcast radio, TV or video; it could be some form of radio control where the radio function is not immediately obvious.

The general name for unwanted radiations from a transmitter is 'spurious emissions', and there are two broad categories:

1. Harmonically related spurious emissions, which are usually called simply 'harmonics'.
2. Non-harmonically related spurious emissions: these are usually just called 'spurious' or 'spurii'.

Harmonics will always be present in any transmission, and in fact the harmonic content of a signal is simply an indication of the distortion of the sine wave which constitutes that signal. An absolutely pure sine wave would have no harmonics in its make-up, but this would be an ideal situation which does not occur in practice (Fig 4.4).

In practical radio work the aim is to reduce the harmonics to a level where they are insignificant compared to any legitimate signals which may be using the frequencies on which the harmonics fall. Many amateurs will remember the days of VHF TV, when the harmonic output of HF transmitters had to be reduced to a level where they were small compared to fringe-area TV signals. Since the decline of VHF TV, the incidence of harmonic interference from HF transmitters has greatly lessened but it can still occur, and may raise its head again if other vulnerable services start to use old VHF TV bands.

Non-harmonically related spurious emissions are usually unwanted mixer products, generated by the heterodyning processes which are used to generate the output frequency in modern transceivers. In adverse circumstances these leak through the various filters, and end up being radiated (Fig 4.5). Transverters are particularly prone because of the additional mixing process involved.

There is another type of spurious emission, which used to be very common, and this is the unwanted products of multiplier stages. In this technique the operating frequency is achieved by multiplying up from a relatively low

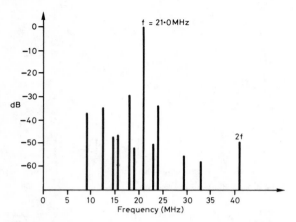

Fig 4.5. Spurious mixer products. Spectrum of a poorly adjusted QRP transmitter

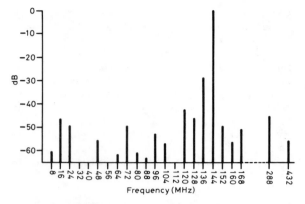

Fig 4.6. Multiplier products. Spectrum of a 144MHz transmitter in which an 8MHz oscillator output is multiplied up to 144MHz. Harmonics of the 8MHz oscillator mix with one another to produce spurious outputs

frequency oscillator, and the unwanted products arrive at the output by a process of harmonic generation and mixing. This oscillator/multiplier process is still occasionally used, particularly in simple CW or FM transmitters, and is worth keeping in mind when investigating problems in vintage or homebrew equipment (Fig 4.6).

All the above mentioned spurii are usually relatively small in amplitude – unless the transceiver has been grossly misaligned – but there is a totally different class of spurious emissions which can give rise to large unwanted signals being radiated. This is oscillation due to instability, caused by some stage of the transmitter oscillating at a frequency which may be quite unrelated to the normal operating frequency.

Spurious emissions are discussed in greater detail in Chapter 6, where for convenience the two categories have been labelled 'predictable spurious emissions' and 'instability'.

Evidence of spurious emissions

Before spending time on more detailed investigations, confirm that the interference disappears when the transmitter is operated into a dummy load – if it is still there, the spurious is leaking out of the transmitter by some means other than the antenna, and this should be dealt with directly as a transmitter problem (see Chapter 6).

If a spurious emission from your station is causing interference in a neighbour's house, then it is likely that similar equipment, tuned to the same frequency and located nearer to your station, will also be affected. If the interference is to radio or TV, there will be no problem in finding a receiver for checking purposes. It may be necessary to rearrange antenna conditions on the test receiver to achieve a comparable pick-up of the spurious signal. Most households have battery-operated radio receivers and many can muster a portable TV. This makes the situation very straightforward. Where the interference is to something not operating on the normal broadcast bands, the problem is first to find out on what frequency the affected equipment is operating, and then to listen round that frequency on a suitable receiver. There is an added complication in the case of radio control equipment, where there may be only one example in the locality, making our question 'Is similar equipment tuned to the same frequency affected?' meaningless, and we have no means of knowing whether the problem is breakthrough or spurious emissions. Nowadays, breakthrough is a much more common cause of interference than transmitter spurious emissions. In cases where there is no clear evidence to the contrary, it is reasonable to start by assuming that breakthrough is the likely culprit.

In general, where a spurious emission problem is suspected, the first step is to get hold of a receiver which covers the frequency of the affected equipment, and use this to listen for any spurious signals. If you are lucky enough to have access to a proper measuring receiver or, better still, a spectrum analyser, checking for spurious emissions will be a positive pleasure. (Contrary to popular belief the construction of a spectrum analyser, quite adequate for this type of diagnosis, is not beyond the average home constructor, and is a very worthwhile project [2].) Most of us, however, will have to fall back on a receiver with a more doubtful performance. It is most important to make sure that the test receiver is set up a reasonable distance from the suspect transmitter and its antennas, otherwise it will be overloaded and create all sorts of internally generated spurious signals. Even in favourable situations where there is no overloading problem, it is always necessary to bear in mind that all receivers have spurious responses of their own and these can easily be misinterpreted.

Recognising the dangerous trouble maker

It is generally true to say that spurious emissions caused by harmonics and mixer products, once detected, are fairly straightforward to deal with, either by realigning or perhaps modifying the transmitter, or by fitting the appropriate filter to the transmitter output. The really serious problem arises when instabilities in the transmitter give rise to oscillations which can be of very large amplitude – in very bad cases comparable to the nominal transmitter power. Older amateurs will remember when most transmitters were homebrew, and one of the main design features was achieving stability in the power amplifier and driver stages.

Similar problems can still occur in modern equipment if sufficiently misused, and the result can be very large unstable signals being radiated which can cause widespread interference. On the HF bands 'widespread' could mean hundreds, or even thousands of miles. Needless to say, the authorities in all countries take a very dim view of this sort of thing.

Fortunately, with modern, well-designed transceivers, instability is rare unless the equipment has been tampered with or has been inexpertly repaired. Be particularly wary if power transistors have been replaced with 'near equivalents'. When instability does occur it often (but by no means always) reveals itself by bad signal reports, particularly on CW, and by erratic output power as the drive power is increased or as the load is changed – for instance by small adjustments of the antenna tuning unit (ATU). In valve amplifiers erratic anode tuning is a common symptom of instability, and should always be investigated.

If you have any reason to think you may have such a problem, go off the air until you are sure that all is well. Again, the best way to check is to use a spectrum analyser but, failing this, carefully tune a receiver over as much of the RF spectrum as possible – at least from the medium-wave broadcast band up to several times the transmitter frequency – to see if there are any large spurious signals. Oscillations due to instability usually sound very rough and are easily identified. Start by checking the transmitter into a dummy load, but don't forget that changes of loading can cause instability to come and go. As before, make sure that the test receiver is not overloaded – in these circumstances you have enough problems without confusing yourself with false receiver responses! If you haven't got the facilities to carry out the sort of check single handed, the alternative is to arrange an 'organised signal test' as described in Chapter 6.

Needless to say, the most dangerous oscillations are those near enough to the wanted frequency to be radiated efficiently by the antenna. This can occur either through direct instability at the signal frequency or by a relatively low frequency parasitic oscillation, which beats with the

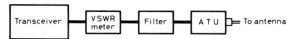

Fig 4.7. Position of the filter. The ATU ensures that the filter sees a 50Ω load

output frequency to give a 'comb' of spurious outputs surrounding the carrier at multiples of the parasitic frequency. This type of parasitic oscillation can occur in transistor amplifiers where the gain of transistors increases as the frequency decreases. The high gain at low frequency can lead to oscillation unless care is taken in the circuit design and adjustment.

It is worth reminding ourselves that the UK licence requires the amateur to check his station from time to time to ensure that its performance is technically adequate, with particular reference to the 'suppression of unwanted emissions'.

The direct approach

In many instances the very facts of the case point directly to the culprit. If radio or TV interference is occurring only on frequencies which are harmonically related to the transmitter frequency, there is not much doubt that the problem is harmonic radiation. Examples are the fourth or fifth harmonic from the 144MHz band, causing interference to UHF TV, or the second harmonic of the 50MHz band, giving trouble at the higher end of the VHF radio band. In such cases it is quite legitimate to go straight to the fitting of the appropriate filter to the output of the transmitter – though the prudent operator, however confident, will confirm the diagnosis with a borrowed filter before rushing off to buy one.

There are two important things to remember about fitting filters to transmitters. First make sure that the filter is suitable for the power in use, preferably with a bit in hand, and second make sure that the filter is correctly loaded: in most cases this means that it must 'look' into 50Ω. On VHF and UHF this is usually provided directly by the antenna system, but on HF an ATU may be needed. The filter is fitted between the transmitter and the ATU, as in Fig 4.7.

In modern HF transceivers, the VSWR meter is often incorporated into the transmitter itself. Its function is to facilitate tuning the ATU to ensure that the transmitter sees a 50Ω load. It is possible for a VSWR meter to generate harmonics – though usually at a low level – and for this reason it should always be connected between the transmitter and any filter which may be fitted.

Types of filter

There are three basic types of filter: band pass, high pass and low pass.

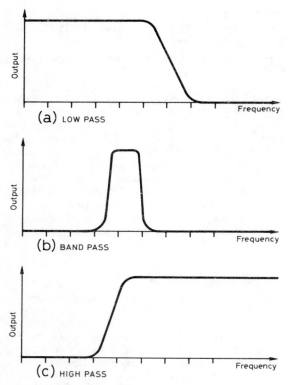

Fig 4.8. The three types of filter

many cases it will be sufficient to clear up harmonics and spurious mixer products – provided that the latter are not too close to the carrier.

The low-pass filter

This is the commonest type of filter, and at one time was considered essential in any HF set-up – again, this goes back to the days of VHF TV. A low-pass filter, as its name implies, will severely attenuate all frequencies above the cut-off frequency. On HF, for instance, this would be about 30MHz. It is still good practice to include a low-pass filter in an HF station, particularly if you have any reason to be doubtful of the transmitter harmonic performance [5].

On VHF a low-pass filter is an alternative to a band-pass filter if the spurious emissions are harmonics, and therefore above the carrier, rather than mixer products which may be either above or below the carrier.

The high-pass filter

This type of filter is the reverse of the low-pass filter in that it attenuates all frequencies below the cut-off frequency. It is not normally used in the output of a transmitter, since any filtering action it might perform would be better done by a band-pass filter. High-pass filters are often used in conjunction with braid-breaker filters to separate UHF signals from relatively low frequency amateur signals in cases of breakthrough, as discussed in Chapter 5.

References

[1] *Neighbours' Questions Answered*. A pamphlet available from the RSGB.
[2] 'Simple Spectrum Analyser', R Blackwell, *Radio Communication* November 1989. (This article is reproduced in Appendix 2.)
[3] *VHF/UHF Manual*, G R Jessop (ed), RSGB, Chapter 6.
[4] 'A simple way to design narrow-band interdigital filters', I White, *Radio Communication* February 1984.
[5] 'A low-pass filter for high power', G Eddowes, *Radio Communication* August 1989.

The band-pass filter

Where a transmitter/antenna system serves only one band, as is common on VHF and UHF, a band-pass filter is practical. This has very little loss for wanted signals in the relevant band, but severely attenuates any signals which are outside the band. There are a number of good designs for home-constructed VHF and UHF band-pass filters; more information can be found in references [3] and [4].

On HF the ATU is a form of band-pass filter, and it is well worth considering using one as part of normal good practice. Usually the filtering effect is limited, but in

SUMMARY

The three charts

Charts 4.1 and 4.2 start with the two questions:

1. Is the equipment some form of radio device suffering interference on specific frequencies?
2. If so, is other similar radio equipment tuned to the same frequencies also affected?

From this point further questions are asked which, with luck, will direct the investigator in the right direction.

Cases which do not give simple answers

Where the answer to both questions is not a clear-cut 'yes' or 'no', it means that the problem probably falls into the 'IF and intermodulation' category.

IF and intermodulation problems

1. Direct breakthrough into the IF of a receiver.
   (a) The fundamental of a 10.1MHz transmitter getting into the 10.7MHz IF of a VHF receiver.
   (b) IF breakthrough into satellite TV receivers (Chapter 9).
   Treat these as cases of breakthrough.

2. Harmonics of an amateur transmitter being picked up in the IF of a receiver.
   (a) The second harmonic of 18MHz, breaking through into the IF of a susceptible TV receiver.
   (b) The third harmonic of 3.5MHz breaking through into the 10.7MHz IF of a VHF radio receiver.
   Treat these as cases of excessive transmitter harmonics.

3. Image interference. The common example of this is signals from amateur transmitters operating on the 1.8MHz band causing image interference to medium-wave broadcast receivers.

4. Amateur signals beating with harmonics of the local oscillator or other oscillators in the susceptible equipment to give spurious responses.

Conditions 3 and 4 will give interference which is tuneable at the receiver, but are really cases of breakthrough and should be treated as such.

Breakthrough is a much more common cause of interference than transmitter spurious emissions, so in cases of doubt it is reasonable to start by assuming that the problem is breakthrough, and to proceed down Chart 4.1.

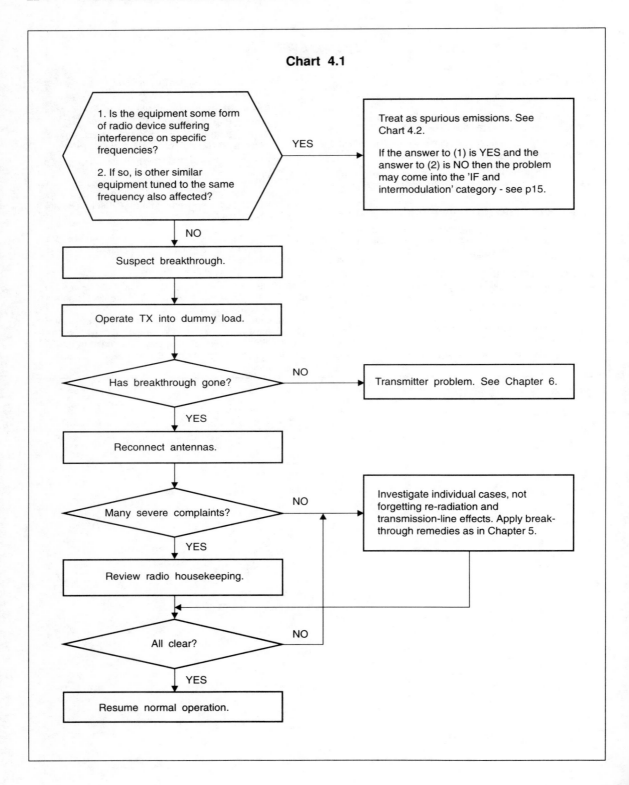

Chart 4.1

1. Is the equipment some form of radio device suffering interference on specific frequencies?

2. If so, is other similar equipment tuned to the same frequency also affected?

YES →

Treat as spurious emissions. See Chart 4.2.

If the answer to (1) is YES and the answer to (2) is NO then the problem may come into the 'IF and intermodulation' category - see p15.

NO ↓

Suspect breakthrough.

Operate TX into dummy load.

Has breakthrough gone? — NO → Transmitter problem. See Chapter 6.

YES ↓

Reconnect antennas.

Many severe complaints? — NO → Investigate individual cases, not forgetting re-radiation and transmission-line effects. Apply break-through remedies as in Chapter 5.

YES ↓

Review radio housekeeping.

All clear? — NO

YES ↓

Resume normal operation.

Chart 4.2

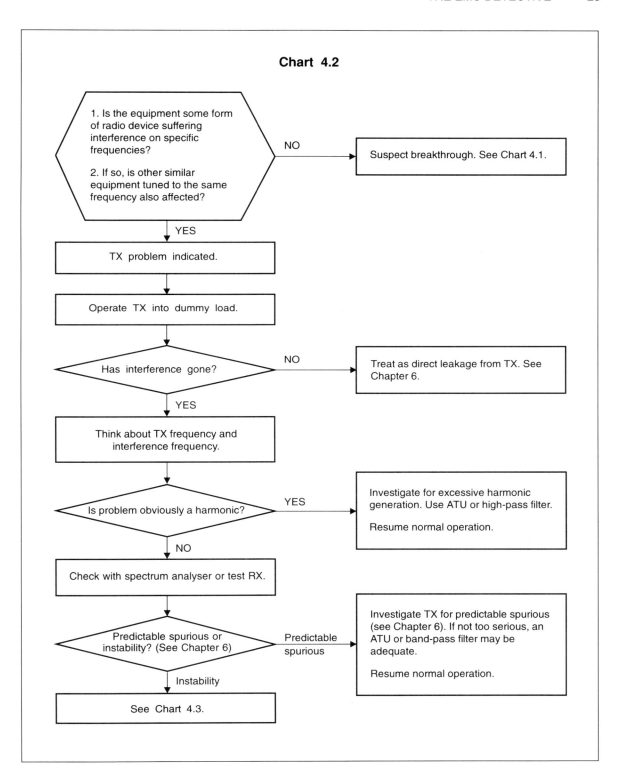

1. Is the equipment some form of radio device suffering interference on specific frequencies?

2. If so, is other similar equipment tuned to the same frequency also affected?

NO → Suspect breakthrough. See Chart 4.1.

YES

TX problem indicated.

Operate TX into dummy load.

Has interference gone?   NO → Treat as direct leakage from TX. See Chapter 6.

YES

Think about TX frequency and interference frequency.

Is problem obviously a harmonic?   YES → Investigate for excessive harmonic generation. Use ATU or high-pass filter.

Resume normal operation.

NO

Check with spectrum analyser or test RX.

Predictable spurious or instability? (See Chapter 6)   Predictable spurious → Investigate TX for predictable spurious (see Chapter 6). If not too serious, an ATU or band-pass filter may be adequate.

Resume normal operation.

Instability

See Chart 4.3.

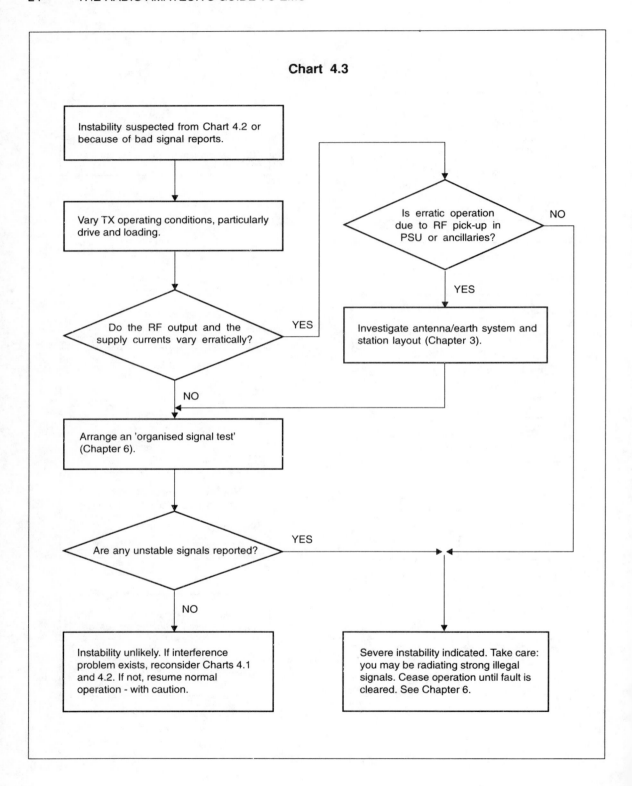

Chart 4.3

Instability suspected from Chart 4.2 or because of bad signal reports.

Vary TX operating conditions, particularly drive and loading.

Do the RF output and the supply currents vary erratically?

Is erratic operation due to RF pick-up in PSU or ancillaries?

NO

YES

Investigate antenna/earth system and station layout (Chapter 3).

YES

NO

Arrange an 'organised signal test' (Chapter 6).

Are any unstable signals reported?

YES

NO

Instability unlikely. If interference problem exists, reconsider Charts 4.1 and 4.2. If not, resume normal operation - with caution.

Severe instability indicated. Take care: you may be radiating strong illegal signals. Cease operation until fault is cleared. See Chapter 6.

Chapter 5

Breakthrough

PART 1 – THE BACKGROUND

Breakthrough has already been discussed in previous chapters, and one may be forgiven for asking why this particular aspect of EMC gets so much attention. The answer is simply that breakthrough is by far the most prominent problem in amateur radio, not only because it is so prevalent but also because it involves other people, and the way it is tackled directly affects public attitudes to our activities. Amateur radio is full of challenges and breakthrough is one of the most exacting. Compared to it, doing well in the NFD contest pales into insignificance, and taking the Morse test is a pleasant meeting of friends.

In this chapter we assume that the basic detective work has been done, and that we are reasonably confident that breakthrough is the problem. In the real EMC world it is not possible to be more than reasonably confident about the mechanism of any case of interference – absolute certainty is a thing which rarely comes the EMC detective's way. The personal problems which arise from breakthrough are often greater than the technical ones, and this very tricky subject is discussed in Chapter 8.

What causes breakthrough?

Practical radio communication always involves both transmission and reception. Breakthrough is simply unwanted reception. The underlying principles governing the reception of signals are the same whether they are welcome or not, and it is worthwhile spending a little time looking at the mechanism of signal pick-up before proceeding to specific remedies.

Imagine that we have a piece of electronic equipment – it could be a TV, a hi-fi or a controller of some kind, but for simplicity let's call it a 'black box'. RF energy can get into the box by two basic routes: either by direct pick-up of signals by the circuitry inside the box, or through external leads acting as an antenna.

Direct pick-up can only take place if the box is made of plastic or wood, or other non-conducting material. Even then the energy involved is likely to be small, unless the frequency is high enough for the wiring inside the box to make an 'antenna' which is a significant fraction of a wavelength, and generally this means frequencies above 50MHz. On the HF bands, where the wavelength is relatively long, ingress through external leads is much more common.

Leads acting as antennas

In considering the mechanism of pick-up via external leads, it should be remembered that RF energy does not just leak into the black box, like water filling a tank. As with any other electrical circuit, the energy must be going to somewhere from somewhere. In other words, electric charges are passing in and out of the box, giving up some of their energy to the internal circuits as they do so. In some instances, the leads form a crude dipole in which the charges oscillate backwards and forwards, inducing RF currents into the circuits inside the box, but it is more common for the currents to flow into the box from leads acting as an unbalanced antenna. In this case the circuit is completed by some sort of earth connection – usually via the mains or by direct capacitance to earth. This capacitance will be between the conductors and metalwork comprising the box and any external earthed objects, including the earth itself. The capacitance to earth cannot be calculated using the standard 'parallel-plate' formula often quoted in connection with capacitors used as circuit components. Due to fringe effects, the true capacitance will be considerably larger – as is mentioned in Chapter 3 in relation to antenna capacitance.

Any wire suspended in an electromagnetic field will act as an antenna, and electric charges will oscillate backwards and forwards in the wire in sympathy with the electric field. The amount of energy which can be extracted depends on two factors:

(a) How the wire is lined up in relation to the electric field. (See Chapter 2.) However, in many breakthrough situations the polarisation of the field is so confused by reflections and re-radiation that for all intents and purposes it can be considered randomly polarised. In this case there will always be quite a lot of signal pick-up whichever way the wire is aligned.

(b) How well the load is matched to the antenna.

The tuned antenna

When the intention is to make an efficient receiving antenna, the loading is arranged to cancel out any reactance and to provide a resistive termination which matches the source resistance. In ordinary radio parlance the antenna is 'tuned to resonance', and 'matched to the load'. In this condition the antenna will extract energy from its 'capture area' (See Chapter 2.)

The high-impedance load

At the other extreme from the ideally matched antenna, we have the situation where the dipole is terminated in a load which is of such a high impedance that it is effectively an open-circuit. If we take the simple case of a short dipole parallel to the electric field, the voltage (V) at the terminals is about half the antenna length multiplied by the field strength (E).

$$V = E \times L/2 \text{ volts}$$

where L is in metres and E is in volts/metre. Modern active antennas exploit this principle, usually using field-effect transistors to give a very high input impedance, and the signal voltage is converted down to 50Ω using the active devices to provide the required output power.

Pick-up in practical breakthrough cases

In real breakthrough situations, pick-up occurs through a combination of the above effects, almost always made more complicated by local re-radiation and transmission-line effects from the mains wiring and other conductors which form an integral part of the modern house. In fact the EM field pattern in such cases is so confused that any attempt to quantify breakthrough signals would be doomed to failure. Fortunately it is only necessary to identify where the unwanted signals are coming from, and then to prevent them entering the susceptible equipment.

Fig 5.1 gives some idea of the path that an interfering signal might take if our black box were an alarm of some kind, operated from the mains supply, having a sensor connected to it by (unscreened) twin cable several metres long. It is reasonable to suppose that the twin cable will act as one antenna but, since one of the conductors is connected to the 0V rail, RF voltages will be injected into the amplifier by the RF current passing through the impedance of the 0V connection on its way to the power supply (PSU), and thence to earth via the mains lead or through stray capacitance. It does not matter whether the power supply has a mains earth connection or not – there will be an adequate path through various capacitances.

In some instances the amplification may take place at RF, particularly where modern audio transistors are used, since these often have gain up to tens or even hundreds of megahertz. In other cases the RF is detected at the first semiconductor and then amplified as an audio signal. As

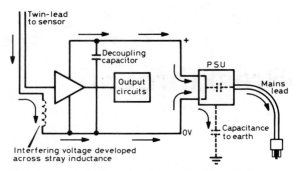

Fig 5.1. Path of RF signal in a typical sensor/alarm device

usual in EMC problems, neither of these effects are likely to be clear cut.

Keeping the RF out

There are two basic ways to keep RF energy from getting into sensitive circuits. The first is by choking the lead or leads which are acting as antennas outside the box, and the second is by bypassing the signals at the sensitive points on the circuit inside the box. The second technique will be dealt with first, and is included mainly as food for thought for anyone building or modifying their own equipment. It is not recommended as a general EMC troubleshooting procedure, except for qualified technicians. As a general rule, it is most unwise to do any work inside equipment which is not your own. You could be letting yourself in for a lot of trouble; in particular you could be held responsible in the case of accident – with disastrous consequences.

Bypassing techniques

Bypassing of unwanted RF is only applicable where leads are carrying DC or low-frequency AC. It is really just a special case of decoupling, and as with all decoupling there are two factors to consider:

1. To use a capacitor which gives the lowest possible impedance to the unwanted signal.
2. To find the correct place to connect the 'earthy' end of the capacitor.

For most requirements a ceramic capacitor between 1nF and 10nF will be satisfactory, and it should be connected with the shortest possible leads – remember that a typical lead 2.5cm long has an inductance in the region of 20nH ($0.02\mu H$), so that any significant length of lead will increase the effective impedance of the bypass path. It is also possible for the lead inductance to resonate with the capacitor, causing unpredictable effects at high frequencies.

The second point is more problematic, because it is not always easy to decide where the correct 0V point actually

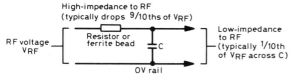

Fig 5.2. The principle of bypassing or decoupling

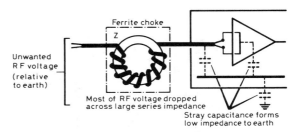

Fig 5.4. The series choke. The impedance of Z forms a potential divider with stray capacitance

is – particularly if the requirement for short capacitor leads is to be realised. Generally speaking, the 'earthy' end of the capacitor should go to the point to which the amplifier 0V connection is made, and to which its inputs are returned.

In some instances it may be possible to use a small ferrite bead, such as the FX1115, threaded on the lead to give an impedance for the capacitor to 'work against' – as in Fig 5.2. This is the classic decoupling circuit, where a potential divider is formed so that the majority of the unwanted voltage is dropped across the series impedance, and very little appears across the bypass capacitor. If circuit conditions permit, it may be possible to use a low-value resistor in place of the ferrite bead. A standard RF choke – as opposed to a ferrite bead – could be used, but this is not recommended as high-Q inductors can give rise to resonance effects. In practice, there is always some source impedance due to lead inductance etc, so that bypassing can often be quite effective without any added series element.

Fig 5.3 illustrates good bypassing and decoupling practice: leads are kept as short as possible, and the 0V rail should be of very broad track or, if practical, a ground plane should be used.

Choking-off the unwanted antennas

As has already been said, the fitting of internal bypassing components is not practical as a general EMC troubleshooting procedure, but fortunately it is possible to achieve the same results in a much more acceptable way. If a high impedance is connected in series with the lead acting as an unwanted antenna, outside the black box, then the internal shunt capacitance and resistance –

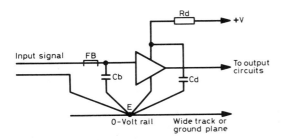

Fig 5.3. Good bypassing or decoupling practice. FB: ferrite bead. Cb: bypass capacitor ≈ 1nF (short leads). Cd: decoupling capacitor (short leads). Rd: decoupling resistor. E: common 0V point – all connections to E to be as short as possible

either intentional or accidental, we don't care which – will cause the majority of the unwanted RF energy to be dropped across the series impedance, and hence only a small residue finds its way into the box. Fig 5.4 gives an idea of the situation which could occur in our black box. The thing that makes this technique so practical is that the series impedance can be provided by a suitable home-made ferrite choke, thus avoiding any modifications to the equipment itself.

Ferrites

Ferrites turn up all over the place in modern circuits, but despite their popularity they are not well understood. This is most likely because they do not fall easily into any simple category of everyday materials.

Many solids have a crystalline structure, but magnetic materials are special in that the crystals are divided into 'domains' in which the atoms themselves are aligned so that their magnetic fields reinforce one another, giving the domain an overall magnetic polarity. A disadvantage of most magnetic materials is that they are good conductors of electricity, so that eddy currents make them unusable at frequencies above a few kilohertz. Ferrites are manufactured from magnetic materials, chemically combined so that they are effectively non-conductive but still possess the required crystal structure for domain formation, and hence they have a relatively high permeability.

When a ferrite is not in a magnetic field, the polarities of the various domains tend to cancel one another, and the overall effect is zero. When a field is applied, the atoms of each domain try to align themselves with the field, mutually interacting so that domains which are more favourably aligned grow at the expense of their neighbours until a dynamic balance is reached. All this takes time, and the net result is that ferrite materials are relatively slow to respond to a changing magnetic field. Just how slow depends on the chemistry of the particular material. Generally, ferrites which have large domains have a high permeability but are slow to respond. In electrical terms this slowness is a loss; energy is used to

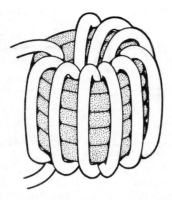

Fig 5.5. A stack of four rings. Thin cable is shown so that the core stack can be clearly seen

align the domain, but before the action is complete, the next half-cycle comes along and the domain tries to align the other way. The losses increase markedly as the alignment time become a significant part of a half-cycle.

The trade-off between permeability and loss enables manufacturers to produce ferrites with a wide range of properties. In the present case we require a material which gives us adequate permeability, and also sufficient loss to dampen any resonances. In effect the choking impedance will be a mixture of inductive reactance, and resistance due to losses.

Ferrite chokes

So far as EMC is concerned, the most popular form of ferrite device is the toroid or ring. A choke is formed by winding a number of turns of the lead in question on to the ring. In most cases as many turns as possible are wound on until the ring is about two-thirds full. This enables the ends of the winding to be kept apart to minimise stray capacitance across the winding. (The self-capacitance can be further reduced by winding the turns as in Fig A4.3, Appendix 4, and this may give improved attenuation, particularly at higher frequencies.) One of the advantages of a ferrite toroid is that a relatively high inductance can be formed with a small number of turns. This is partly due to the toroidal shape forming a good magnetic path, and partly to the fact that ferrite materials can be made with high permeability.

How many turns?

The inductance of a coil is proportional to the square of the number of turns – that is, twice as many turns will give four times the inductance – and a turn on a toroidal core means every time the wire goes through the hole in the ring. Since in practice there is a limit to the number of turns that can be accommodated on one ring, it is often

convenient to use two or more cores to increase the inductance as in Fig 5.5. As a rule of thumb, for choking HF signals, the number of rings in the stack multiplied by the square of the number of turns should be about 400, though at 21MHz and above a figure of 200 is more appropriate. Typically, we might have 14 turns on a two-ring stack. For VHF fewer turns should be used – approximately seven turns on a single ring will be satisfactory at 144MHz.

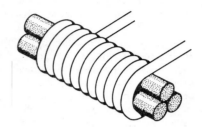

Fig 5.6. Cable wound on three ferrite rods

The ferrite ring is the most effective core for a choke, but in some instances it is not possible to use a ring – usually because of large connectors which cannot be removed. A fairly effective choke can be made by winding the lead on a length of ferrite rod salvaged from the antenna of an old medium-wave radio. For thick leads, a convenient arrangement is to use three lengths of rod taped to form a core of roughly triangular cross-section as in Fig 5.6. The rod (or rods) should extend at least a centimetre or two beyond the windings, as this has a significant effect on the inductance. Generally, rod chokes are not very effective at frequencies below about 10MHz, unless a large number of turns is used – 20 or more if possible.

A range of split ferrite cores has become available. These consist of a 'ring' which is actually a square shape, made in two halves that can be clamped together when the winding has been completed. Where no manufacturer's information is available for these, reasonable results will be obtained by using the winding guide given above for ferrite rings.

Types of ferrite

It is important to use the correct type of ferrite core, otherwise results will be unpredictable. The last thing that the investigator wants is to end up trying different chokes in front of an audience who may be all too ready to be unimpressed. Many rings do not have any identification marks, and the best way to ensure that you get the right type is to purchase them from a reliable supplier who is selling cores specifically for EMC purposes.

More information on ferrite rings will be found in Appendix 3.

Checking ferrite rings

Ferrites are complicated materials and not easy to charac-terise, but as a quick check of whether an unknown ring is likely to make a practical choke or not, the 'series-loss' test will be found useful. This circuit is also quite a good illustration of how the choke operates in practice.

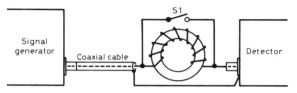

Fig 5.7. Ferrite choke test circuit

Wind 10 turns of insulated wire on to the ring, and connect the ends of the winding between a signal genera-tor and some form of detector as in Fig 5.7.

The signal generator and the detector should have 50Ω output and input respectively. If there is any doubt about this, a 6dB attenuator should be inserted either side of the test circuit to define the source and load resistance. (Further information on attenuators will be found in Chapter 6 and Appendix 5.) The switch and the terminals for the choke (and the attenuators, if required) can be mounted on a plastic box. Tune the signal generator to a frequency of about 3.8MHz and switch S1 from closed to open; the difference indicated on the detector between the two conditions should be at least 8dB. Repeat the test at 28MHz: the difference should be greater than about 23dB. The best detector would be a spectrum analyser, but any of the RF detectors discussed in Chapter 6 could be used. If the detector is uncalibrated, the difference can be measured by re-adjusting the signal generator output so that the detector output returns to some pre-determined level.

Common-mode and differential signals

In many cases the cable wound onto the toroid will have more than one conductor: it may be a mains lead, or perhaps a length of flat twin or twisted pair carrying audio or the output of a sensor. It is sometimes asked how the choke can act on the unwanted RF while not affecting the normal use of the conductors in the cable.

Where two or more conductors are very close together compared to the wavelength of an RF field, then they are effectively one conductor – or in our case one unwanted antenna. The unwanted RF currents flow up and down them together, creating a magnetic field which is the same as would exist round a single conductor. Currents of this type are known as 'common-mode' currents, and are dealt with by the normal action of the ferrite choke. Where a signal (in our case the wanted signal) is between the wires, as in Fig 5.8, currents which are equal in magnitude, but opposite in direction, flow in the wires. Because the wires are close together, or in electrical terms 'closely coupled', the magnetic fields at any point except in the space between the wires tend to cancel – effectively confining the field between the two wires. Since there is no significant external magnetic field from these differ-ential signals there is no inductive action, and the signals pass through the ferrite choke unaffected.

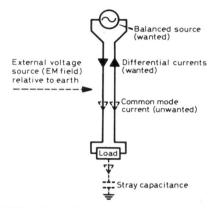

Fig 5.8. Differential-mode and common-mode currents

In a coaxial cable, the wanted signals are carried by the fields confined between the inner conductor and the inside of the braid, and are completely isolated from the effect of the ferrite ring. The unwanted currents effec-tively flow on the outside of the braid, and see the high impedance of the choke.

Screened cables

Where a pair of wires is screened, the common-mode currents will flow on the screen and the differential signals will travel on the inner conductors. It is important that the screen should be connected to the correct point on the circuit, otherwise it might do more harm than good. The screen should be connected to the 0V rail at the point to which the inputs are referred (point E in Fig 5.3). Ideally this should be a thick piece of track or, better still, a ground plane. Where the case of the equipment is made of metal (or possibly plastic with a conductive coating) it should be bonded to the same point. In EMC investiga-tions conditions are often far from ideal, and it may be found that trouble is caused by RFI entering the equip-ment via the screen. Where this is the case, a ferrite choke should be fitted as near to the susceptible equipment as possible to provide a high impedance to currents on the screen. The situation is very similar to that which exists with TV and radio coaxial feeders, and this is dealt with in some detail later in this chapter.

PART 2 – BREAKTHROUGH TO SPECIFIC EQUIPMENT

So far we have looked at factors which are common to all breakthrough situations, and it is now time to get down to brass tacks and consider specific problems. Traditionally, the major EMC problem in amateur radio is breakthrough to TV and radio and, though nowadays the radio includes audio gear of various types, this is still true. It is not surprising that this should be so, when it is considered that this type of equipment involves high-gain amplifiers, coaxial feeders crying out to act as unwanted antennas and, most important of all, that it is to be found in almost every home.

A complication with all types of radio-based equipment is the likelihood of intermodulation and cross-modulation, added to the classical breakthrough modes of direct amplification and rectification. Apart from the confusion that might arise in distinguishing breakthrough from transmitter problems – as discussed in Chapter 4 – these effects do not alter the anti-breakthrough procedures. Whatever the mechanism of the interference generation inside the susceptible equipment, our object is to keep the unwanted signal out.

Things should change for the better when the new EC standards, which lay down the requirements for the immunity of domestic equipment, become effective. This will involve the ability to withstand reasonably large (unwanted) signals applied to all the external leads, including the braid of the coaxial feeder and the mains lead. As mentioned in Chapter 3, the regulations are quite complicated, but if we assume immunity to signals at levels of a volt or two we will be in the right region for most practical purposes. It is important to note that the regulations do not require every item of equipment be tested to prove compliance – this would be quite impractical – so that it is always possible (though unlikely) for any particular set to have a manufacturing fault which makes it unusually susceptible.

Be prepared

The complexity of practical EMC investigations is legendary, but the situation can be made much less formidable by a well-organised approach, and this will have the added bonus of impressing third parties that you know what you are doing – even if it isn't completely true. Where an installation is complicated, make a sketch along the lines of Fig 5.12, leaving room to make comments on the effectiveness (or otherwise) of the different chokes. Make sure that you have all that you are likely to need before starting – a list of suitable items is given in the summary at the end of this chapter. Try to arrange any visits to allow plenty of time, so the job does not have to be rushed. The other vital preparation is to make arrangements for test transmissions from your own station. If at all possible enlist the help of another amateur, and set up a reliable means of communication – a couple of 144MHz or CB handheld transceivers are ideal. When using the handheld transceiver, keep a reasonable distance away from the equipment being investigated, thus avoiding any spectacular breakthrough or possibly damage (real or imaginary) from this source.

TV and video cassette recorders (VCRs)

In a TV installation the most vulnerable point is the antenna input, and in the majority of cases eliminating unwanted signals at this point will clear up the problem. The most common route for the unwanted signals to get in to the set is via the braid of the coaxial feeder. The small size of UHF TV antennas makes it unlikely that large signals will be picked up directly by the antenna and be propagated down the coaxial feeder as a normal received signal, unless the frequency of the interfering signal is relatively high – above about 100MHz or so. When interfering signals are picked up on the braid of a TV or radio feeder, it is usual to assume that the currents flow only on the braid, and that the inner conductor is unaffected. This is not really true: the actual flow of common-mode current will depend on the conditions at each end of the feeder (as seen by the interference), complicated by the skin effect. Fortunately, for practical purposes it is quite adequate to take the simple view that the currents flow on the braid and that the object is to reduce or eliminate them.

First have a look at the general installation. Are the coaxial connectors correctly fitted with the braid firmly gripped and making good electrical contact with the outer connection of the plug? TV coaxial connectors are designed to be used with different diameter cable and there is no unanimity as to the correct way to fit them. Figs 5.9(a) and (b) show the two generally accepted methods. Make sure that the centre pin is properly soldered – this is a point often missed by busy installers, but it is well worth doing. Apart from a potential intermittent contact, subsequent oxidation can cause a rectifying junction, giving rise to unexpected interference effects.

Corrosion of the connector at the end of the cable coming down from the antenna may mean that water has got into the cable and worked its way down into the connector. The commonest cause is chaffing or splitting of the sheath, allowing water to enter, though it could be a failure of the seal at the antenna itself. Whatever the cause, a cable which is corroded will show a marked increase in loss at the TV frequencies but, more important from the EMC point of view, the individual wires of the braid make poor contact with one another, reducing the overall screening performance. A corroded or disconnected screen will have effects similar to those discussed in Chapter 9 (Fig 9.2). The solution is to replace the cable

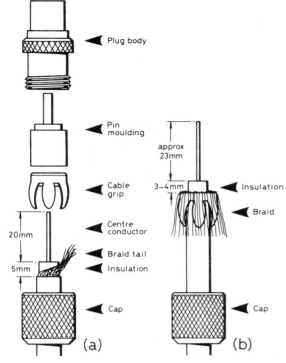

Fig 5.9. Two methods of fitting domestic TV coaxial connectors. (a) Wrap the braid tail round the 5mm of inner insulator and push cable grip down on to it, ensuring that whiskers of braid do not short to the centre conductor. (b) Braid is 'teased' out, bent back over cable grip and cut off

and possibly the antenna, though it may be difficult to persuade a neighbour – who probably has not noticed the deterioration in TV performance – that the expenditure is justified. The best way of proving that the antenna system is at fault is to connect the TV to a different antenna, located in more or less the same place. This may not be as difficult as it might seem at first sight; there may be an independent TV antenna feeding another set in the same house – in the children's room or a 'granny flat' for instance, and connecting across would only require a reasonable length of TV extension lead. It is important to remember to fit a ferrite-ring choke if a long extension lead is used for test purposes – otherwise pick-up on the braid could confuse the issue. If it is necessary to move the TV or VCR to another room, make sure that the owner is in charge of the operation, and that the question of insurance has been considered – just in case the worst should happen.

Antenna amplifiers

In recent years, the fitting of various types of signal booster amplifiers has become increasingly popular, and

these have their own EMC problems. Amplifiers are usually fitted for two reasons: either because the signal is very weak, or because the feeder losses are excessive. In many cases these two reasons amount to the same thing – the antenna is mounted as high as possible because the signal is weak, and this results in a long coaxial feeder with a relatively high loss. In either case, the only sensible place to locate the amplifier is right at the antenna. Amplifiers of this type usually have a good noise figure – many of the more modern ones use a GaAs FET (gallium arsenide field-effect transistor) as the active device.

A well-designed masthead amplifier, which is correctly installed close to the antenna, is unlikely to give problems at HF because the length of unwanted antenna will be limited, but at VHF conditions could be very different. Problems arise if the unwanted signal reaching the input to the amplifier device is large enough to drive it into non-linearity and cause cross-modulation. Once this has taken place, there is nothing that can be done at ground level to correct it. If a masthead amplifier is suspected, the only practical way to prove it is by substituting antennas as discussed above. Masthead amplifiers get their DC power supplies through the coaxial feeder, so that any filters or braid-breakers must pass (and not short-circuit) the required DC current. Unless specific information is available, it is best to use only ferrite ring chokes in the down leads from such amplifiers.

Indoor amplifiers are much more likely to cause problems, especially where HF is concerned, but fortunately they can easily be removed from the circuit for test purposes. An amplifier in this position, of course, does nothing to overcome cable losses but, because of the good noise figure of the amplifier, it may improve the signal-to-noise performance of the TV receiver. Some amplifiers have several outputs, allowing more than one set to be operated from the same TV antenna without the losses involved in passive splitters. If the amplifier has to be retained in the installation it should be considered as part of the TV set (or sets), and the standard techniques using chokes and filters on the antenna side of the amplifier will still apply. Typical arrangements are shown in Fig 5.10.

Chokes and filters for TV installations

The simplest way of choking-off signals travelling down the braid is to use our old friend the ferrite ring choke; used in this way it is often called a ferrite ring 'braid-breaker'. There is a practical problem making them, in that the coaxial cable most commonly used for UHF TV is too thick to be wound conveniently on to the core. Added to this, low-loss TV coaxial feeder uses cellular polythene dielectric, which can allow the inner conductor to short-circuit to the braid if the cable is forced into a tight winding. It is best to make the choke separately, using a

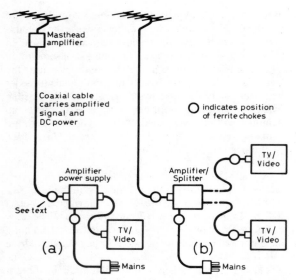

Fig 5.10. Fitting chokes to an antenna amplifier. (a) Masthead amplifier. (b) Indoor amplifier feeding two TV sets

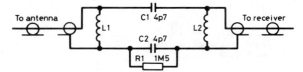

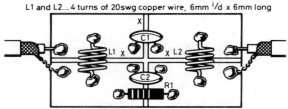

L1 and L2....4 turns of 20swg copper wire, 6mm i/d x 6mm long

X ..... approx 1·5mm wide grooves cut in copper foil to leave four areas as shown.   2in x 1in single-sided printed-circuit board.

Fig 5.11. Combined braid-breaker and high-pass filter. R1 is a static discharge resistor. Connections from the coaxial cable to the PCB must be as short as possible

length of smaller-diameter coaxial feeder with suitable TV connectors at each end – usually a plug at one end and a socket at the other, as in Photo 5.1. For HF break-through, about 12 to 14 turns on a stack of two cores gives a practical choke, and seven turns on two cores should be satisfactory for VHF up to about 100MHz. Above that, seven turns on a single core will be adequate. The coaxial cable used for the choke should, of course, be 75Ω, but there is no need to use low-loss cable since the length involved is quite short. Don't forget to test the choke for continuity and freedom from short-circuits before you use it in earnest – it can be embarrassing to find these things out when you are performing before an audience!

Another form of braid-breaker is shown in Fig 5.11.

This has the advantage of incorporating a high-pass filter, which will attenuate HF and VHF signals which may be passing down the coaxial cable in the normal way (between inner conductor and the inside of the braid). The small capacitors C1 and C2 are part of the high-pass filter, so far as the TV signals are concerned, and a high series reactance at HF, giving the filter its braid-breaker action. Care should be taken in checking the performance of the TV after installing a home-built filter of this type, as some degree of discontinuity to signals coming down the coaxial feeder is inevitable. This has been known to cause unexpected problems, particularly on teletext. For obvious reasons, this type of braid-breaker cannot be used where the coaxial cable is also supplying DC power to a masthead amplifier.

Try the chokes and filters in order, starting with the antenna choke (F1 in Fig 5.12). Do not remove a device if it does not seem to work – in many cases of break-through, the unwanted signals enter the installation by

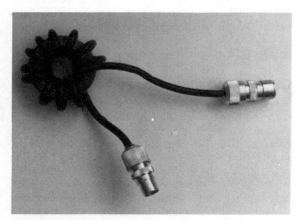

Photo 5.1. A ferrite ring choke suitable for TV coaxial down lead

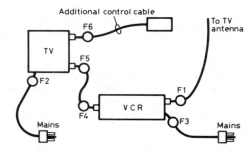

Fig 5.12. Typical domestic TV installation, showing positions of ferrite chokes. F1: antenna coaxial feeder choke (or filter). F2/F3: mains chokes. F4/F5: coaxial chokes on RF lead (VCR to TV). F6: Choke on additional leads to controls or external speakers or displays

more than one route, and the observed interference is the result of the signals adding or subtracting. If a ferrite choke is only partially successful, another should be tried in series to increase the rejection but it is usually not worthwhile to go beyond two. When the sources have been identified, chokes which are not needed can be removed. Actually the order of trying chokes does not matter too much, so long as things are done in an organised way – but it is important to start with the antenna.

The chokes fitted to the mains leads (F2 and F3 in Fig 5.12) are made by winding the cable onto a pair of rings in the same way as a ferrite-ring braid-breaker. It goes without saying that in this case it is essential to avoid damaging the cable in any way. If the cable is unusually thick it may be necessary to use fewer turns and more rings. For the HF bands, the rule that the square of the number of turns multiplied by the number of rings must come to about 400 applies. For dealing with VHF breakthrough, a smaller number of turns should be used. Because of the closed magnetic circuit in a toroidal core, it is not necessary to pull the cable tight onto the ferrite material; all that is required is for the winding to be secure and the ends not too close together. If it is not possible to use ferrite rings – because the plug cannot be removed, for instance – then a ferrite rod choke can be used, though the choking effect will not be so great, particularly on the lower HF bands. Alternatively a split core can be used.

Chokes may be needed on either end of the coaxial cable between the VCR and the TV set, depending which unit is susceptible. If you are unlucky and the lead is abnormally long, they may be required at both ends. Some modern TV installations have additional control and audio cables connected to either the TV or the VCR, and these should be dealt with in the same way as the mains leads. It is reasonable to expect the owner of the equipment to disconnect non-essential ancillaries during the diagnostic process, and where ancillaries are gimmicky and poorly engineered, it may have to be accepted that it is not practical to expect such a system to operate without interference.

Specific problems associated with satellite and cable TV are dealt with in Chapter 9.

Commercial braid-breakers and filters

Braid-breakers and filters are available from a number of commercial manufacturers, and these are usually very effective provided that the correct type is used. Some devices are simply braid-breakers, with no filtering of signals travelling down the inside of the coaxial cable, while others include high-pass or band-stop filters optimised for specific bands, so it is important to study the specification before making a decision. In some instances it may be necessary to use two devices – for instance a braid-breaker in series with a high-pass filter – to achieve

Photo 5.2. A commercial filter fitted to the antenna feeder lead of a TV set

the desired rejection. Further information on braid-breakers and filters can be found in Appendix 3.

At the time of going to press, the RSGB keeps a stock of suitable filters supplied by a reputable manufacturer, and details of current devices and prices can be found in *Radio Communication*. These filters have the advantage of being unobtrusive, as shown in Photo 5.2.

There are many types of commercially manufactured mains filters on the market, but not all are effective in dealing with breakthrough. Generally, filters which do not provide a high impedance on all the mains input wires – live, neutral, and earth (if used), will not give much protection, since the unwanted RF currents usually flow in and out of the equipment as a common-mode signal, and not differentially between the wires. The best thing is to start by trying a ferrite-ring choke, and not to use a commercial mains filter unless a special need arises. In any case, examine the specification of the filter carefully before committing yourself.

Radio and audio equipment

In general, the approach to radio and audio problems is the same as that for TV, though there are differences of emphasis. Interference caused by the braid of the antenna coaxial cable acting as an unwanted antenna is still a serious problem, but the larger elements on VHF broadcast antennas makes direct pick-up of interference (which is then passed down the coaxial cable in the normal way) more likely.

The speaker leads of a stereo system frequently pick up interference which is transferred to the input of the amplifier, either through stray capacitance or through negative-feedback networks. The leads should be choked by winding them on to ferrite rings or alternatively, if this is not possible, on to lengths of ferrite rod or split ferrite cores.

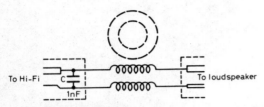

Fig 5.13. Twin speaker lead wound on ferrite core to make plug-in choke unit

One way of simplifying on-site operations is to have chokes already made up. These consist of a length of lead wound onto a ferrite ring, with connectors fitted at both ends. With this technique it is possible to make a very neat arrangement, and since the wire diameter can be chosen to suit the application, it may be possible to use a smaller ferrite ring than would otherwise be possible. A small ceramic capacitor of about 1nF (1000pF) can also be included at the end which is going to plug into the main equipment, as shown in Fig 5.13. This should be done with caution: too large a value could lead to instability and possible damage to the equipment. If you are not familiar withe the audio equipement in question, it is safer to leave the capacitor out. Make sure the connectors are correctly wired and that there are no short-circuits; some hi-fi units can be damaged if operated into open- or short-circuit loads. This technique can be used on other leads, such as those going to a tape deck or a record deck, but in this case the capacitors should be smaller – about 100pF is typical. Again, do not include the capacitor if there is any doubt about its effect in the performance of the equipment – in most cases the choke will be adequate on its own. As with a TV, the remaining control and mains leads should be fitted with whichever type of ferrite choke is practical.

Where breakthrough to a portable radio is experienced, there is not very much that can be done from the outside of the set since there are no external leads to choke, but fortunately it is usually possible to find a location where the interference is negligible. Frequently portables only give trouble when operated from the mains, and this is a clear indication that a ferrite choke is required on the mains lead.

The human factor

The annoyance caused by radio interference to audio equipment depends very much on the mode in use. AM or SSB is worst in this respect since, once the RF is detected, it will almost inevitably be amplified and delivered to the speakers as a distinctly audible signal. FM is much less troublesome, and usually manifests itself only by a click as the transmitter is switched on and off. Likewise, the

data modes based on frequency-shift keying (FSK) should also only give clicks, though in some techniques they occur fairly frequently. In annoyance rating CW comes somewhere between SSB and FM since, though the clicks occur at the keying rate (which is fairly high), there is no other amplitude modulation. The audible effects can be minimised by ensuring that the keying waveform of the transmitter has long enough rise and fall times – about 5 to 10ms is reasonable.

Interference to alarms and control electronics

At one time this type of breakthrough was rare enough to be the cause of jokes at club 'natter nights', but the huge increase in problems of this type has completely changed attitudes. The effects of local radio transmissions on electronically controlled household appliances is now a serious problem.

There are so many possible types of equipment which might be affected, with new designs appearing almost every day, that it is only possible to deal with general principles. In effect the first part of this chapter has already done this, in the discussions of the 'black box'. The whole problem revolves around the ingenuity required to tailor the procedures outlined to fit a particular situation. In some instances, it may be possible to make up ready-made choke units which can be plugged in, as suggested for audio equipment.

If you are installing the gear yourself the answer is to make sure you buy the equipment from a reputable supplier (with the appropriate BS number or the CE logo), and make sure that good installation practice is used. Even in equipment which has already been installed, it may be possible to improve matters by looking for sources of local re-radiation or transmission-line coupling – see Chapter 3.

Telephones and associated equipment

The first thing to check is whether the equipment is rented from a company or authority which undertakes to correct breakthrough, free of charge, as part of normal service. If this is so, make sure that you deal with the appropriate department – breakthrough is not all that common, and the receptionist at the service or complaints department may be unaware of the company's policy.

Specific information on dealing with breakthrough to telephones will be found in Chapter 9.

Intractable cases

It is inevitable that some cases of breakthrough will prove too difficult to solve. In some instances the problem will be social rather than technical, and it is difficult to advise on such a situation. We all know from everyday experience that people can vary from extremely helpful to almost insanely awkward. Chapter 8 looks at the various problems and makes some suggestions on lines of approach.

Where a case fails to yield to the procedures we have been discussing in this chapter, it is time to call for some help, and in most cases this means contacting your national society. In the UK, the RSGB's EMC Committee has set up a country-wide network of EMC co-ordinators. Their addresses and telephone numbers are published at frequent intervals in *Radio Communication* and also in the *RSGB Amateur Radio Call Book* [1]. The idea is that a member with an EMC problem should first try the standard remedies and, if these are unsuccessful, the co-ordinator should be contacted. If the co-ordinator cannot advise on a suitable solution, the problem will be passed on to one of the EMC Committee's specialists who deals with that particular aspect of EMC. Needless to say, this procedure does not guarantee a successful outcome in every case, but at least the technical advice given will be the best available and, most important of all, it will be impartial.

If a piece of equipment is clearly very susceptible to breakthrough, the manufacturer should be consulted, though how one should go about this varies from country to country. In the UK it is best to take the matter up with the retailer first, and it is the owner of the equipment who should make the approach – not the amateur. If this does not lead to a satisfactory outcome, the local co-ordinator should be contacted and the general situation discussed. It may well be that the equipment in question is a well-known source of trouble and there is a precedent for dealing with the manufacturer.

Reference

[1] *RSGB Amateur Radio Call Book*, RSGB.

SUMMARY

The causes of breakthrough

(a) *Direct pick-up by circuits inside the 'black box'*. This will only take place if the box is made of non-conductive material – usually plastic – and if the interfering frequencies are high enough for the internal circuitry to form an antenna which is an appreciable fraction of a wavelength.

(b) *Pick-up by external leads acting as crude dipoles*. The best example of this is speaker leads on a stereo hi-fi system.

(c) *Pick-up by external leads acting as antennas relative to earth*. This is a very common situation, the earth path being either through the mains lead or via capacitance to ground.

Keeping the RF out

There are two ways to keep RF energy out of sensitive circuits:

(a) *By providing a path that has a low impedance to RF energy, effectively bypassing the input of the sensitive circuit*. This approach is appropriate when building equipment, but is usually not practical as a general EMC troubleshooting technique.

(b) *By greatly increasing the source impedance by using a ferrite choke on the input lead and relying on internal shunt resistance and capacitance to act as the lower half of a potential-divider circuit*. This technique has the great advantage that it does not require any modifications to the equipment itself, and it is the only practical procedure in most cases.

Types of ferrite choke

There are three types of ferrite chokes commonly made by amateurs. These are:

(a) *The ferrite ring choke*. This is made by winding a number of turns on to the ring until it is about two thirds full. The actual number of turns required depends on the core material and the number of rings in the stack. As rule of thumb for HF, the square of the number of turns times the number of cores in the stack should be about 400. For VHF above 100MHz about seven turns on a single ring will be satisfactory.

(b) *The split-core choke*. This is similar to the ring choke, except that the core is a square rather than a ring, and is made in two parts which can be clamped together after the winding is completed. The manufacturer's instructions should be followed regarding the number of turns required. Where no information is available, use the same rules as for ferrite rings.

(c) *The rod choke*. Where requirements are not too exacting, a useful choke can be made by winding the lead onto a piece of ferrite antenna rod from an old AM radio. For thicker cables, three lengths of rod can be taped together to form a core of roughly triangular cross-section. A dozen or more turns should be used, and if possible the core should be considerably longer than the coil so that it sticks out at least 15mm at each end. A choke of this type will have less impedance than either a ring or a split-core choke, but can be very useful especially at frequencies above about 10MHz.

(continued)

SUMMARY – CONTINUED

Things to check In a domestic installation

(a) *Badly made coaxial connections*. Make sure that all coaxial connectors are correctly fitted and that the centre pin is soldered.

(b) *Corroded connectors on antenna down leads*. This probably indicates that water has entered the cable and worked its way down under the insulation.

(c) *Antenna amplifiers*. A large signal arriving at an amplifier can cause cross-modulation, and give rise to interference which cannot be removed at a later stage in the system. This is much more likely in the case of an indoor amplifier located near the TV, because the braid of the coaxial feeder acts as an unwanted antenna. In general, any of the chokes or filters prescribed for TV antenna down leads can be used in front of an indoor amplifier (though reference should be made to Appendix 3 where reservations are expressed regarding the use of notch filters in front of TV amplifiers). With a masthead amplifier, remember that the coaxial lead between the amplifier and the power unit carries the DC power up the cable as well as bringing the signal down, so in this lead only chokes which pass the required DC current can be used. A simple ferrite-ring choke is the best choice if there is any doubt, since to DC this is really no different from the coaxial cable itself.

A typical breakthrough kit

(a) One combined braid-breaker and high-pass filter for TV frequencies – either a home-made item as in Fig 5.11 or a suitable commercial device. Where operation is confined to specific bands, it may be worth having a special filter for those bands.

(b) One ferrite-ring choke braid-breaker, with a TV co-axial connector at each end.

(c) Two back-to-back TV coaxial cable connectors, for joining lengths of coaxial cable together.

(d) Two ferrite rings, for making chokes.

(e) A length of TV coaxial cable with connectors at each end.

(f) Two lengths of ferrite rod from old medium-wave broadcast radios, for making rod chokes. Two suitable split ferrite cores would be a good alternative.

(g) Audio connectors and other items to make up plug-in chokes as in Fig 5.13.

(h) Odd useful items such as spare TV coaxial plug, 'phono' plug, insulating tape, small cable ties, lacing cord etc.

Procedure

(a) In radio and TV installations, always start with a braid-breaker (and possibly a filter) in the antenna coaxial cable – more often than not this will cure the problem straight away.

(b) Do not remove a choke or filter if it does not immediately cure the problem. Leave it in place until some chokes in other leads have been tried and results assessed.

(c) Be calm and business-like, and try to keep your temper, however aggravating the audience may be!

Chapter 6

Transmitter problems

PART 1 – SPURIOUS EMISSIONS

During the first quarter of the last century, a French civil servant retired from public life to devote his time to what had always been his main preoccupation – scientific investigation. In the course of this work he discovered a theorem which made his name famous ever after throughout the world of science and engineering. The gentleman in question was Jean Baptiste Joseph Fourier, and his theorem concerned the analysis of periodic functions into component parts. The application which is familiar to all radio enthusiasts is that every wave can be broken down into a sine wave plus harmonics. When Fourier propounded his theorem he was actually investigating the nature of heat, but the idea that the sine wave is the simplest entity in any waveform comes into all branches of science. In more complicated situations, such as a modulated radio frequency signal, the output will be a combination of several waveforms, but these can always be broken down into the component sine waves and their associated harmonics.

The time and frequency domains

These expressions frequently appear in radio textbooks, and are a prime example of something which sounds very impressive, but is really quite a simple concept. We are so used to thinking of waves in the form shown in Fig 6.1(a) that we tend to forget that this is only a graphical representation of a variable – usually voltage or current – which is changing in amplitude as we move along the 'x' axis. If x is time, as it usually is, then the representation is said to be in the 'time domain'. The typical oscilloscope trace of an RF voltage is in the time domain.

There is another way of representing waveforms where the x axis is not time, but frequency, as in Fig 6.1(b). This is the 'frequency domain'. As we go from left to right, the amplitude of the signal is plotted against increasing frequency. This principle is exploited in the spectrum analyser, an instrument which is now considered almost indispensable in radio laboratories and workshops.

When the subject of composite waves is discussed, newcomers occasionally question the reality of the components. For instance, in an AM signal, it might be asked whether the varying carrier actually exists or whether only the constant carrier and side bands really exist. All too often the answer given is that the constant carrier and sidebands can be proved to exist mathematically, and the impression is left that, in some way, the carrier varying in amplitude is something of a fiction. The fact is that all the manifestations have equal reality; it all depends on whether you are looking at the time domain or the frequency domain. It is rather like someone being both daughter and wife – the situations are not incompatible, they are just the answer to different questions. The lady is a daughter in the 'parent domain' and a wife in the 'marriage domain'.

The quest for a pure signal

In amateur radio a high priority has always been given to signal quality. In the early days this was probably due

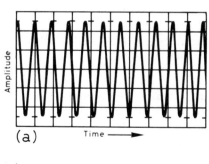

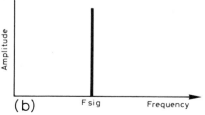

Fig 6.1. (a) A sine wave displayed on an oscilloscope – the time domain. (b) A sine wave displayed on a spectrum analyser – the frequency domain

37

simply to pride in producing the best possible signal; but as years went by the emphasis on signal purity as a way of minimising interference, both to fellow amateurs and also to other services, became increasingly important. In today's crowded radio environment it is, without doubt, the most important feature of transmitter design. The aim of any design must be to produce the desired RF output, occupying only just enough bandwidth to encompass the required modulation, with no energy radiated on any other frequency. This is, of course, an ideal situation which can never be achieved in practice, but a really well-designed transmitter can come surprisingly close to it.

The two major considerations in approaching the ideal are, first, the basic technique chosen to generate the final radio frequency and, second, how much time and money is to be spent on good practice in implementing the chosen technique.

In addition to spurious emissions caused by the frequency generation process, which are predictable (at least in principle), there are others which are not. These fall into the general category of instability, and are due to unintentional feedback causing oscillation in some stage of the transmitter. Fortunately such instabilities are fairly rare in modern transceivers but, because of their unpredictability in both frequency and magnitude, when they do occur, they can cause very serious problems. In this chapter, the two categories have been labelled 'predictable spurious emissions' and 'instability'.

Predictable spurious emissions

As has already been said, these depend on the technique used to generate the final frequency. There are three basic techniques used in amateur transmitters.

1. Mixing the output of two oscillators together to produce a third frequency. A practical transmitter may employ several mixer stages in order to achieve the required output frequency.
2. Starting with a relatively low-frequency oscillator and multiplying the frequency by factors of two or three in successive stages, until the required frequency is reached.
3. Direct generation at the final frequency, using a low-level oscillator, and amplifying the signal up to the required output power.

The mixer or heterodyne method

This has gradually taken over as the standard technique of signal generation in amateur transmitters. There are several reasons for this, but the most cogent is that there is really no other practical way of achieving SSB output on the different HF bands.

A glance at the block diagram of any modern commercially built amateur transceiver shows that the mixing processes used are quite complex, usually involving

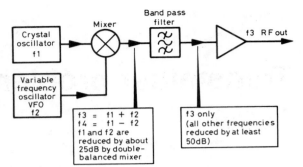

Fig 6.2. A simple mixer frequency generator

several mixer stages. To some extent, the complexity is due to the combining of the transmit and receive functions, particularly where the modern trend of making the receiver tuneable over the whole HF band is followed. It is unlikely that anyone would embark on the design and construction of a complex transceiver without a thorough study of the engineering problems or, more probably, a design taken from a reputable journal or handbook. However, a brief look at a simple example of the use of a mixer in frequency generation will help indicate where troubles can arise.

Fig 6.2 shows the outline of the simplest possible mixer transmitter. The principle is that the fixed oscillator is mixed with the output of the variable frequency oscillator (VFO) to produce the sum or difference of f_1 and f_2, giving a third frequency f_3. In a practical mixer, f_1 would be the heterodyne oscillator, and would be of larger amplitude than f_2. Let's suppose that we want to cover the 14MHz band, and we have to choose suitable frequencies for f_1 and f_2. As well as the sum and difference of f_1 and f_2, all the intermodulation products will be present at the output of the mixer, and the design task is to arrange the two frequencies and the selectivity of the band-pass filter to ensure that only the wanted frequency is present in the output. Anything other than the wanted RF output will be a spurious signal, and if radiated could cause interference.

Table 6.1 lists the intermodulation products generated by two frequencies; of course the list goes on *ad infinitum*, but the significance of the product becomes less as the order increases. If for the fixed oscillator (f_1) we choose a frequency of 9.000MHz, and for the variable oscillator (f_2) a frequency range of 5.000MHz to 5.500MHz, the sum of these would cover 14.000 to 14.500MHz, but we need to check all the intermodulation products from Table 6.1. For instance, taking the third-order product $2f_1 - f_2$, we see that it will fall into the band 13 to 12.5MHz, and we must now ask ourselves whether the filter will have sufficient selectivity to eliminate this. Certainly a simple tuned circuit would not be good enough, as can be seen from Fig 6.3. This case emphasises the benefit of using a double-balanced mixer such as the diode ring in

Table 6.1. Intermodulation products produced by two frequencies

Fundamental	Second order	Third order	Fourth order	Fifth order
f_1	$f_1 + f_2$	$2f_1 + f_2$	$3f_1 + f_2$	$4f_1 + f_2$
f_2	$f_1 - f_2$	$2f_1 - f_2$	$3f_1 - f_2$	$4f_1 - f_2$
	$2f_1$	$2f_2 + f_1$	$3f_2 + f_1$	$4f_2 + f_1$
		$2f_2 - f_1$	$3f_2 - f_1$	$4f_2 - f_1$
	$2f_2$	$3f_1$	$2f_1 + 2f_2$	$3f_1 + 2f_2$
			$2f_1 - 2f_2$	$3f_1 - 2f_2$
		$3f_2$	$4f_1$	$3f_2 + 2f_1$
				$3f_2 - 2f_1$
			$4f_2$	$5f_1$
				$5f_2$

Example: Frequencies if f_1 = 9.0MHz and f_2 = 5.0MHz

9.0	14.0	23.0	32.0	41.0
5.0	4.0	13.0	22.0	31.0
	18.0	19.0	24.0	29.0
		1.0	6.0	11.0
	10.0	27.0	28.0	37.0
			8.0	17.0
		15.0	36.0	33.0
				3.0
			20.0	45.0
				25.0

Fig 6.4(a), as opposed to an unbalanced type such as the dual-gate FET mixer shown in Fig 6.4(b). A double-balanced mixer tends to cancel many of the unwanted outputs, including $2f_1 - f_2$, allowing some relaxation on the filtering requirements.

If a circuit of this type gives unexpectedly high spurious

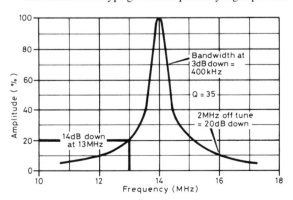

Fig 6.3. Response of single tuned circuit $2f_1 - f_2$ (18 – 5MHz = 13MHz) attenuated by only 14dB

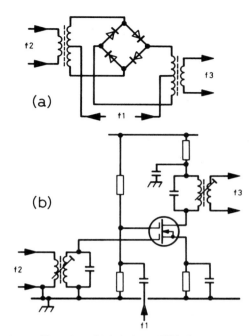

Fig 6.4. (a) Ring mixer. (b) A dual-gate FET mixer

outputs, check the level and waveform of the signals feeding the mixer – where frequencies are relatively low quite a modest oscilloscope will be adequate for the purpose. If these seem to be in order, look for faults in the mixer or the filter. In a brief discussion it is impossible to do justice to the fascinating subject of mixers and their intermodulation products, and further information will be found in [1].

The multiplier method

This was the traditional technique for both amateur and commercial HF transmitters, and was almost universal until the coming of SSB in the late 'fifties and early 'sixties. It was very well suited to the valve technology of the time, but suffered the fatal disadvantage that it did not lend itself to SSB. In general, this technique will not be encountered today except in vintage equipment or in simple homebrew equipment such as a CW HF transmitter, or possibly in a VHF FM transmitter. Fig 6.5 shows the outline of a transmitter for the 21MHz band. The variable frequency oscillator (VFO) covers 3.5 to 3.575MHz, and this is multiplied by two in the first multiplier to give 7.0 to 7.15MHz. The 7MHz signal is filtered, and then multiplied again, this time by three to give an output at 21 to 21.45MHz. This is filtered and passed on to the power amplifier (PA) and hence to the antenna. In traditional designs the multiplier and filter was simply a valve with a tuned circuit in the anode. The valve was biased well beyond cut-off, and so the relationship between anode

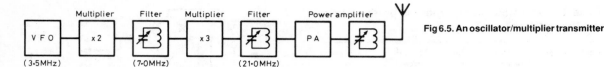

Fig 6.5. An oscillator/multiplier transmitter

current and grid drive was very non-linear. This is a good example of how a non-linear circuit generates harmonics, and is worth studying for this reason alone, even if one has no particular interest in old techniques [1].

When this technique was used, it was common to bias the (valve) PA beyond cut-off (Class C), and to tune and match the anode using a tuned circuit. This points up another fact – that a Class C stage, because of its non-linearity, is a prolific generator of harmonics, and if it must be used, then good filtering is essential.

It is quite possible to select the wrong multiple when tuning up a transmitter of this kind. For instance if, in Fig 6.5, the first multiplier were mistakenly tuned to the third harmonic instead of the second, and then this was again tripled in the second multiplier, the result would be a transmitter covering 31.5 to 32.175MHz! It was to combat this sort of mistake that the requirement for an amateur station to have an absorption wavemeter was originally laid down. Even using modern techniques, it is still possible to accidentally end up on entirely the wrong frequency, and an instrument of this type, particularly if it is combined (as it often is) with a dip oscillator, is a very useful piece of test equipment. It should not be looked upon as just another legal requirement. Information on constructing an absorption wavemeter and dip oscillator (often called GDOs – grid dip oscillators – though they nowadays use transistors) will be found in [2].

Frequency multiplication is often used in modern transmitters and receivers to provide a heterodyning frequency (usually from a crystal oscillator) and it is important to avoid unwanted harmonics from getting past the output filter. The lower the original frequency and the higher the required multiple, then the greater is the filtering problem. Where possible, it is better to use an overtone crystal, rather than the high harmonic of a fundamental crystal. A good example of this is in a 144MHz band transverter where a fifth-overtone crystal oscillator operating at 116MHz might be used to mix with 28MHz to give 144MHz [3]. If a low-frequency oscillator and harmonic generator were used, a large number of out-of-band spurious signals would be created which could well cause interference to essential services, understandably bringing the wrath of the authorities down on the head of the amateur.

Direct generation at the final frequency

This is rarely encountered in amateur practice, except for single-band transmitters operating at 7MHz or below. For this purpose, it is a favourite of QRP home constructors,

and in the hands of an experienced constructor/operator is capable of very satisfactory results. The only points to look out for in this case are oscillator drift and general stability of the design and layout.

With the advent of synthesisers the direct generation of much higher frequencies has become quite practical, and in commercial and military designs which require the coverage of much wider bands than in amateur equipment it is sometimes used to good effect. Generating the carrier in this way means that there are no mixing or multiplying operations and consequently no spurious products. The only spurious outputs are those due to the synthesiser itself, and in equipment of this type the design of the synthesiser is a major consideration. It should, perhaps be said that when the term 'synthesiser' is used in modern amateur radio discussions it always means a digital synthesiser; other types using banks of crystals and mixers etc are of only historical interest. At the present time, most digital synthesisers use either the phase-lock or frequency-lock principle. There is another type becoming more practical as devices get faster in operation, and this is direct digital synthesis. In this method the required frequency is generated directly in the synthesiser chip [4].

In modern amateur equipment, synthesisers are usually used in combination with the mixing technique, giving a very neat and practical way of generating the carrier. The main benefit of the synthesiser is not really improved basic radio performance, but rather ease of control – with digital frequency selection, memories and all the extras which feature so prominently in the advertisements.

How small should predictable spurious emissions be?

All transmitters generate harmonics (or, to be more formal, harmonically related spurious emissions), and all except the very simplest single-band, low-frequency equipment will generate spurious mixer or multiplier products. In a practical transmitting installation not all spurious emissions will be radiated well, because the antenna may not be resonant at that particular frequency. However, since the antenna characteristics are unknown at the transmitter design stage, spurious levels are always quoted for operation into a resistive dummy load. Modern transceivers almost always require a 50Ω dummy load, though some older transmitters were designed for a nominal 75Ω load.

(a)
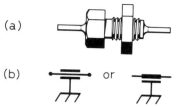

(b)

Fig 6.6. (a) Feedthrough capacitor with thread and nut fixing (solder flange versions are available). **(b)** Circuit diagram

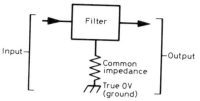

Fig 6.7. Common impedance to ground couples input to output

Emissions are usually quoted in 'decibels with respect to the carrier' (dBc), though sometimes an absolute power or voltage is used. In this case the level will be stated in 'decibels relative to 1mW' (dBm) or as so many microvolts. In amateur radio the use of 'dBc' is almost universal. For HF transmitters, all spurious outputs should be at least 60dB below the carrier (−60dBc), but this may not be good enough where a harmonic falls on to a VHF broadcast frequency, and greater harmonic attenuation will be required in these specific cases. For low-power equipment, coming into the QRP category, some relaxation is permissible, and −40dBc would probably be adequate. With transmitters for frequencies above 30MHz, the aim should be to have spurious levels at least −80dBc, and where a harmonic falls on a UHF TV channel even lower levels may be required.

Reducing predictable spurious emissions

Assuming that the design has been well thought out and suitable heterodyne frequencies have been chosen, then excessive spurious emissions will be due to inadequate filtering or to signals somehow leaking past the filters. Leakage can take place on equipment which originally had a good specification, if it has been repaired or modified – particularly if screens have been tampered with. Check that all wires entering a screened compartment are decoupled; in some instances it may be worthwhile to use feedthrough capacitors. These capacitors have one plate connected to the body, which is soldered or bolted to the wall of the screened compartment, while the other is connected to the feed wire which passes through the capacitor (Fig 6.6). More information on this topic will be found in reference [5]. Generally, there is no point in going to elaborate decoupling techniques unless they are applied to all the leads entering the screened compartment (except RF leads). Screening is like a colander – it is no use carefully blocking up one hole, and expecting it not to leak. The important thing is to make sure that the screening is as comprehensive as possible, and that good RF decoupling techniques are used on all leads.

A frequent cause of leakage past filters is the existence of a common ground return impedance. Where high-performance filters are used, quite a small common

impedance will cause significant leakage (Fig 6.7). The solution is to ensure a low impedance by using printed circuit boards (PCBs) with a substantial ground plane or, where this is not possible, to achieve a similar effect in some other way.

Where simple tuned-circuit filters are used, ensure that taps and link windings are correctly designed to minimise unwanted coupling, and don't forget that the loaded Q of the circuit is considerably less than that of the circuit on its own [1].

Incorrect transmitter operation

A special class of predictable spurious emissions are those caused by incorrect setting up of the transmitter. The most obvious example is the generation of distortion products by misuse of power amplifiers in SSB transmitters. The frequency components in the voice spectrum of an SSB transmission are really separate RF signals, which are individually amplified by the power amplifier. Where several RF signals are handled by an amplifier, there will be some intermodulation between them caused by non-linearity in the amplifier. Practical amplifiers are always non-linear to some degree, and the effect is worsened by overdriving; in extreme cases the amplifier will simply 'run out of steam', and increasing the input results in no increase of output. The odd-order intermodulation products (ie third-order, fifth-order etc) appear around the carrier as in Fig 6.8, causing interference to users of adjacent frequencies [1]. A generally acceptable figure for these products is about −35dBc or lower. The way to

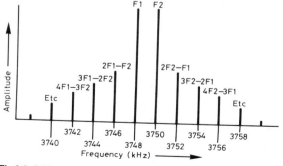

Fig 6.8. Odd-order 'intermods' from a two-tone SSB signal on the 3.5MHz band

achieve this is to ensure that your amplifier is as linear as possible, and to avoid the temptation to increase the microphone input too much.

Modern transceivers have ALC (automatic level control) to maintain the drive at a more or less constant level, and hence avoid overdriving the power amplifier. Most also have signal processing to increase the effective speech power. While it is possible for faults in these circuits to cause unacceptable intermodulation performance (usually called 'splatter'), it is much more likely for such effects to be caused by incorrect operation of the equipment. Study manufacturers' instructions carefully, and check any experimental adjustments by obtaining a reliable signal report. If there is any real doubt about performance, set up an 'organised signal test' as described in Part 2 of this chapter.

So far as CW transmissions are concerned, it is important to use a keying waveform which permits the RF energy to build up and decay over a period of a few milliseconds, so that key clicks are avoided. A similar consideration applies to data modes, where the transmitter is quickly switched from transmit to receive, though in this case there is the added complication of complying with the requirements of the data system in use.

Spurious emissions due to instability

In the present context, instability means something oscillating when it should not. There are two main types of instability which affect transmitters.

(a) Direct instability, where an RF amplifying stage oscillates at, or near, its normal operating frequency.
(b) Parasitic oscillations or 'parasitics' where a circuit oscillates at some frequency which may be quite remote from the operating frequency.

Not everyone would agree about these definitions, but they are a convenient way of identifying the different effects.

Direct instability
This was a common problem in valve transmitters, and one of the prime design features was avoiding feedback from the anode circuits to the grid [1]. This type of problem may still be encountered in vintage equipment, and also in modern valve power amplifiers, but it is not restricted to valves. It can occur with transistors, though the techniques used in semiconductor designs make it less common. This type of instability is perhaps the most dangerous spurious condition, since it is possible to radiate a very large unstable signal on, or near, the normal operating frequency where the antenna can be expected to radiate efficiently.

Fortunately, direct instability is relatively easy to detect, particularly if one has already been alerted to a possible problem by bad signal reports. Sometimes a stage will oscillate when it is not being driven, and this can cause an unstable transmission to take place when the carrier control is turned to minimum, or on SSB when there is no audio input from the microphone. Any unexpected readings on the RF power meter, or on the power supply current meter should be investigated immediately. With home-built equipment, look out for erratic changes in the operating conditions while tuning up the various stages.

When investigating a suspect transceiver, vary the operating conditions, especially the drive and loading. Erratic changes of output or supply current is an indication of instability. However, this does not necessarily mean that the transceiver is faulty. Erratic operation is quite often caused by RF entering the power supply or ancillary control circuits due to poor station lay-out and unsuitable antenna/earth arrangements (see Chapter 3). In fact, if the transceiver is a commercially manufactured unit of well-proven design, this is a far more likely possibility than instability due to a transceiver fault. It is also important to remember that varying the loading to a semiconductor power amplifier stage can cause protective circuits to come into action and severely reduce the output power.

Parasitic oscillations
These cover a wide range of effects and vary from severe oscillations which will have similar symptoms to direct instability, to low-level oscillations which are difficult to detect. Frequently, a low-frequency parasitic makes itself known by beating with the carrier to give sidebands. This sometimes happens in transistor RF amplifiers, where the gain of the device is much greater at low frequencies than it is at HF or VHF, so that any unintentional feedback causes oscillation at frequencies of a few megahertz upwards. This oscillation and its harmonics beat with the signal that the stage is intended to amplify, causing a comb of spurious outputs. To avoid this, circuits should be designed with due regard to the low-frequency conditions, as well as optimising the RF performance. Pay special attention to decoupling and consider using two capacitors: a small one suitable for HF or VHF as required, and a larger one for low frequencies. VHF parasitics can occur in HF transmitters, and these beat with harmonics of the carrier to give outputs in the HF band. This tendency to beat and form a large number of spurious signals means that it is usually fairly easy to detect the presence of parasitics, particularly as they almost always have a very rough, unstable-sounding note [6].

In valve amplifiers it is common practice to include parasitic stoppers in grid and anode circuits [1]. In some applications an anti-parasitic choke is formed by mounting a carbon composition resistor inside a coil. When investigating problems in a vintage transmitter, it is worth checking that these resistors have not become open-circuit or suffered a radical change of value through age or misuse. (Suitable carbon-composition resistors are becoming hard to find, so it is worth acquiring any which may turn up at rallies or junk sales.)

Parasitic oscillations sometimes occur in the most unexpected places, such as audio amplifiers and power supplies. Modern designs frequently use devices which have a high open-loop gain in circuits where the overall gain is controlled by external feedback components. Incorrect choice of feedback conditions or poor decoupling can lead to oscillation. In effect, there is some frequency at which the gain and phase conditions are such that parasitic oscillation can take place. It is most important to look at the manufacturer's data and recommendations when using integrated amplifiers and similar devices, and arrange the circuit so that the device is always operated in the recommended gain range. Good layout and decoupling are also essential; don't be fooled into thinking that because the circuit is dealing with DC or audio frequency that layout does not matter. The parasitics don't know that it is a low-frequency circuit!

Direct leakage of the RF from the transmitter

At one time this was a fairly common problem, but is now rarely encountered, probably because of an increasing awareness of the importance of good EMC techniques in both commercial and amateur designs.

The way to minimise leakage is to use good screening and decoupling throughout the whole equipment, and then to enclose it in a metal case which forms as near a complete screen as possible. Holes in the case for controls, indicators or for ventilation should be as small as possible, and where practical covered with a conductive mesh (from the EMC point of view, many small holes are better than one big one). Leads which pass out through the case should be filtered to prevent RF getting out [5]. The mains lead is particularly important, but in this case it is essential to ensure that any components used are suitable for operation at mains voltages.

Mild cases of leakage can be cured by the use of ferrite chokes on the leads which are giving trouble. This will usually be the mains lead, and the techniques are similar to those discussed in connection with breakthrough in Chapter 5. Severe leakage indicates a fault condition. Check for defective decoupling and filtering, and that internal screens have not been damaged or possibly left out altogether.

Before concluding that an interference problem is due to direct leakage, check by running the transmitter into a dummy load (if the interference persists then the problem is leakage). Nowadays it is much more likely that effects which appear to be due to direct leakage are in fact due to

general poor radio housekeeping, causing the transmitter to be 'hot' to RF, and giving the superficial impression of transmitter leakage. This is dealt with in more detail in Chapter 3.

PART 2 – TESTING AND TEST EQUIPMENT
Detecting and measuring spurious emissions

This depends very much on the test equipment at the amateur's disposal, which can vary from almost nothing through to a fully equipped radio workshop. For many amateurs the main interest is operating, with engineering activities confined to masts and antennas; in such cases it is possible to get by with a minimum of test equipment. This means that reliance must be placed on using a transmitter of known good specification, and operating it with due care. If there is any doubt about the levels of harmonics (or other spurious emissions) then a suitable filter should be used (Chapter 4). In particular, take note of any bad signal reports which could indicate that all is not well.

Before looking at test equipment for the amateur whose interest is experimenting and homebrewing, it is appropriate to consider a test procedure which is available to all amateurs, and which is no more than a formalised version of a typical signal report. To distinguish it from a casual report which can often leave much to be desired, this procedure has been called an 'organised signal test'.

The organised signal test

The best approach is to call on the services of an experienced local amateur who can receive your signals at the S9 + 10dB level or greater. If there is no one living close enough, it is possible to set up a receiver a reasonable distance away (a few hundred metres would do) but this is obviously not so convenient. Where practical, it is better to set up a communication channel separate from the receiver or transceiver being used for the test. Two VHF portable transceivers might be suitable for the link. The receiver used for the test must cover the frequencies of interest and must have good selectivity. In effect this means a good IF filter, and where VHF is concerned better results may be obtained by using an HF receiver and a converter. (The congested state of the HF bands dictate that a high-quality IF filter is a 'must' on a modern HF receiver.) The test should be arranged at a time of minimum band activity; on HF, find a time when the bands of main interest are closed for long-distance traffic. In general, this sort of test will not check harmonics or similar predictable spurious emissions which are a long way from the carrier; however, if a wide enough frequency range is available on the receiver (and a wide-band antenna is used), spurious emissions of this type can be revealed. This type of test is really intended to cover three important transmitter faults:

(a) serious instability, direct or parasitic, giving outputs on or near the operating frequency;
(b) transmitter faults and maladjustment, giving rise to splatter in SSB transmissions;
(c) key clicks on CW transmissions.

Carrying out the test

Arrange for the signal level at the receiving end to be as large as possible (at least S9 + 10dB) and then reduce it by adding attenuation at the receiver input, so that the final signal is no greater than about S9. This will ensure a noise-free signal, but one which is not large enough to cause overloading. This latter point is most important: almost all the difficulties with this test come from excessive received signal so that receiver defects are mistaken for transmitter problems. The actual test procedure will depend on the experience of the receiving operator. The following notes are intended only as a guide for those who are unfamiliar with the technique.

When looking for instability, the suspect station should transmit on the appropriate mode, while the receiving station tunes around as far as practical on both sides of the frequency. Problems will be revealed by odd, unstable-sounding signals coming and going in sympathy with the signal being tested.

When the problem is a (supposed) poor-quality SSB signal, the receiving station should tune very carefully about 100kHz on either side of the wanted signal. The signal should fall off sharply outside the normal SSB bandwidth and the intermodulation products which appear above and below the wanted signal should be much smaller than the signal itself. To get a feel for the situation, it may help to visualise the IF pass band as a 'box' being moved up and down the band as the receiver is tuned. The object is to see how much signal is in the box as it is moved to different frequencies either side of the wanted signal, as compared to the signal in the box when it is tuned right on the wanted signal. Where the finer points of signal quality are in question, experience is important; it is easy to confuse defects at the receiving end for problems at the transmitter. Fortunately, where a serious transmitter problem exists, it should not be difficult to identify. When AGC is in use the actual audible level is not very meaningful, and the S-meter should be used to give an indication of relative level, though it should be calibrated against a signal generator for accurate results. To get a subjective assessment the AGC should be switched off but, since the unwanted signals will be unintelligible, it may be difficult to compare levels by ear. Before being dogmatic about the quality of a

signal, check signals from different sources to get the feel of what a good signal should be like.

Detecting key clicks is relatively unambiguous. Tune around the wanted signal to see if any clicks are audible at frequencies a few kilohertz away. There should be no significant clicks once the wanted signal is outside the bandpass of the receiver's IF filter.

Acquiring and using test gear

Where equipment is to be designed and built at home, then the acquisition of test gear is a more important consideration, and can become an interest in its own right. The wide diversity of activities is one of the great strengths of amateur radio, but it makes it difficult to generalise as to what is desirable (from the EMC point of view) in the typical amateur workshop. The following list and discussion is intended to generate ideas, and to give a few hints to anyone who is intending to become involved in experimental homebrewing.

The spectrum analyser

This is the aristocrat of the radio test gear world. Anyone who has access to one will find it invaluable in all sorts of alignment work and, more importantly, it makes the detection and measurement of spurious emissions a relatively simple matter. Unfortunately commercial spectrum analysers are extremely expensive – way out of reach of the typical radio amateur – and it is unlikely that a cheap second-hand one will be discovered, unless it is in very poor condition. Modern analysers are impressive instruments, enabling accurate measurements to be made with the minimum of human intervention, but for most amateur purposes such a level of sophistication is unnecessary.

It is quite practical to make a spectrum analyser which will give good service in the amateur workshop, with a reasonable expenditure of time and money. Appendix 2 is an article reprinted from *Radio Communication*, giving details of a unit which converts an oscilloscope to a spectrum analyser. There is certainly no better way of learning about radio measurements than by tackling such a project and finding out how to get the best out of the resulting instrument.

When making measurements on a transmitter output, the analyser is connected to the antenna socket via a suitable attenuator, as in Fig 6.9. It is most important that the correct attenuator is used – this is not just an academic point, as it is easy to do very expensive damage to the

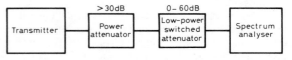

Fig 6.9. Connecting a spectrum analyser to a transmitter

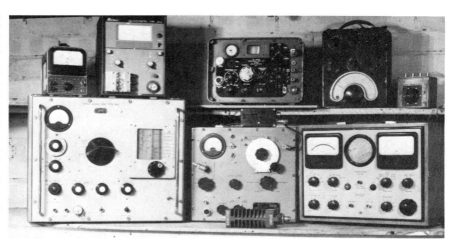

Photo 6.1. Some vintage test equipment in an amateur workshop. Top left to right: LF millivoltmeter (from a few hertz up to about 4MHz, 'sixties); RF millivoltmeter (up to hundreds of megahertz, 'sixties); signal generator (85kHz–30MHz, late 'fifties); signal generator (95kHz to 80MHz, early 'fifties); switched attenuator (75Ω). Lower left to right: wave analyser (30kHz to 30MHz, direct conversion with pre-mixer selectivity, late 'fifties, weight 23kg!); signal generator (100kHz to 80MHz, modified for digital frequency readout, 'fifties); heterodyne voltmeter (superhet with 10.7MHz IF and no-premixer selectivity, late 'sixties). Centre front: power attenuator (nominal rating 50W). Beware – collecting old test gear can be habit-forming!

input circuit if too much RF power is fed into the analyser. Make it a rule always to use more attenuation than necessary to start with, and to remove it when the required level is established. The attenuator must, of course, be able to dissipate the full power of the transmitter. It is usual to use a high-power attenuator adjacent to the transmitter to absorb the power, and to use a low-power switched attenuator at the input to the analyser, to give flexibility for different measurements.

A good rule to remember in connection with attenuators is that 30dB divides the power by 1000, so that you get 1mW out for every watt in, and a further 10dB divides by 10 so that 40dB would give 0.1mW and so on. Another rule to remember is to connect high-power attenuators the right way round – if you connect the output end to the transmitter, the low-power output resistors will almost certainly be burnt out. With low-power attenuators, either end will handle the small dissipation, and it does not matter which way round they are connected.

The measuring receiver

Before the days of spectrum analysers, the standard method of measuring spurious emissions was to use some type of measuring receiver. This is simply a receiver (usually fairly insensitive by communication receiver standards) which can be tuned across the frequencies under investigation. The overall gain is adjusted by switched attenuators, and the signal level displayed on a calibrated S-meter, so that the strength of signals can be accurately measured. Receivers of this type are still used in field-strength investigations and, like all modern professional radio test equipment, are very expensive by amateur standards.

Vintage measuring receivers are sometimes to be seen on sale at rallies and surplus equipment sales and can be a good buy, but great care is needed because many instruments look as if they might be useful but may in fact be quite unsuitable. Ideally, a receiver should have plenty of selectivity before the mixer, and switched attenuation in the front end and in the IF stages. Some designs use direct conversion to audio frequency, and these can be very satisfactory – again provided there is adequate pre-mixer selectivity. The technical practice in the era when these old instruments were in vogue dictated sound construction and relatively simple circuits, so they are usually easy to repair and maintain. The sound construction also means that they are large and heavy. This is no problem if the instrument is purchased at a rally – there will almost certainly be a fellow enthusiast to give a hand to carry it to the car park. Whether the same enthusiasm will be displayed when you arrive home with it is a different matter.

Generally a measuring receiver is used in the same way as a spectrum analyser, and in experienced hands is capable of very good results. The big difference is in the time it takes to look for spurious signals, which on a spectrum analyser are presented directly on a screen.

Sometimes one comes across instruments on the surplus market going under the name of 'selective voltmeters' or 'heterodyne voltmeters'. Generally these were designed with the intention of measuring (with a fair degree of accuracy) signals of known frequency, and often there is no selectivity in front of the mixer. This means that there will be a number of significant spurious responses generated in the instrument itself. These instruments are quite satisfactory for checking harmonics and known spurious emissions, but can be confusing if used to search for unexpected spurious signals.

In any situation where it is not clear whether a signal is coming from the transmitter or is a spurious response in the test receiver, the following check will help to resolve the doubt.

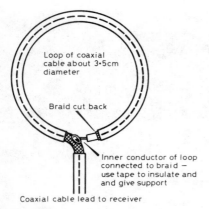

Fig 6.10. The screened loop

Tune in the spurious signal, and connect a tuneable band-pass filter between the attenuator and the input to the test receiver (where the notch filter is in Fig 6.11.). If the spurious signal can be peaked up when the band-pass filter is tuned to the same frequency as the test receiver, the spurious is coming from the transmitter.

Where nothing else is available, an ordinary communications receiver can be pressed into service, provided the shortcomings are appreciated. The most important is that unless the receiver is very well screened and has a means of reducing RF and IF gain it may be impractical to connect it in the transmitter/attenuator arrangement of Fig 6.9. It is very difficult to reduce the leakage of RF energy from a high-power transmitter to a level where sensible measurements are possible. Things are much easier when dealing with 'QRP' designs, or where the low-power stages of a transmitter are being checked.

All receivers have spurious responses, and in general these become more troublesome as the signal level increases. The golden rule is to keep the level of the fundamental signal as low as possible, consistent with being able to detect the spurious signals that you are looking for. When a communication receiver is being used, the fundamental should not be greater than about −40dBm; on a typical HF receiver this will be in the region of S9 + 30dB. S-meters are notoriously inaccurate and should be calibrated against a signal generator (near the frequency of interest) before any credence can be given to the indications. (If no generator is available relative readings can be checked by using a fixed, steady signal, and switching in attenuators at the receiver input.)

Sometimes the only practical possibility is to operate the transmitter being tested into a dummy load, and to arrange the receiver as far away as possible, with a metre or so of wire connected to the antenna input. Needless to say, this will only give the roughest indication of spurious emissions but, carried out carefully, is considerably better than nothing.

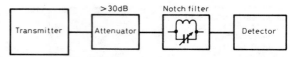

Fig 6.11. Using a notch filter

When looking for the source of unwanted oscillations, a screened loop formed out of a length of coaxial cable, as in Fig 6.10, will be found very useful. It is used with a suitable receiver (or a spectrum analyser if one is available) to find the region where the signal is strongest.

The tuned detector
This is really an improved version of the absorption wavemeter, and depends on a simple tuned circuit to give the required selectivity. Circuits have been devised to reduce the loading on the tuned circuit, and hence to increase the effective Q [7]. Even with such refinements, a simple tuned detector cannot distinguish between signals which are close together, especially if the one being detected is far smaller than an adjacent one, as is usually the case in transmitter tests.

The situation would be considerably improved if the level of the carrier could be reduced without affecting the signals we are trying to measure. This can be achieved, with certain limitations, by introducing a notch filter after the attenuator and before the detector. The general arrangements for using a notch filter are shown in Fig 6.11.

Tuneable notch and band-pass filters
Commercial tuneable filters can be quite complicated (and expensive) but the devices suggested here are about as simple as anything can be in the radio world. The two types of filter shown in Fig 6.12(a) and (b) can be built in a few hours, and the cost will be negligible if a well-stocked junk box is available. The filters should be housed in a metal box, large enough to allow the coil to be mounted at least one coil diameter away from the sides. The components should be mounted so that the leads are

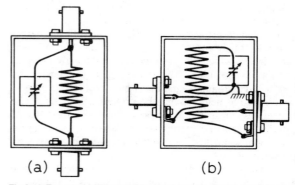

Fig 6.12. Two simple filters. (a) The notch filter. (b) The band-pass filter

as short as possible – particularly those to the coaxial connectors. The position and number of turns on the link windings of the band-pass filter is best found by experiment; a good number to start with is between one-fifth to one-tenth of the number on the main winding.

The notch filter is rather more of a design problem. It is easy to achieve a fairly deep notch, but the important point is to avoid affecting harmonics or other frequencies of interest so far as possible. A good compromise is to arrange for the frequency of interest to tune with a value of capacitance which has a reactance of about 100Ω or so. That would be about 450pF at 3.5MHz or 225pF at 7MHz, and so on up to 56pF at 28MHz. It may seem surprising that a relatively low L to C ratio is used, with the consequent loss of circuit Q, but in this case it is necessary to ensure that away from resonance the reactance of the filter circuit is not too great.

A notch filter can be used with a spectrum analyser or a measuring receiver, and will effectively improve the dynamic range by 30dB or more. This will be particularly welcome in the case of a home-made analyser where the signal handling cannot be expected to match that of the expensive commercial units. It is important to remember that the notch filter will also reduce the level of signals which are fairly close to the carrier, and its use could give a false impression in such cases (Fig 6.13).

The band-pass filter can be used to select a signal for observation, in the reverse process to the notch filter, but because of the different configurations the selectivity is much less. If both filters are to be used together, then it

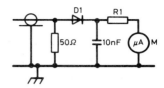

Fig 6.14. A simple detector. R1: select to suit meter. D1: silicon diode, eg 1N4148. M: sensitive meter, 50 or 100µA FSD

may be convenient to use a 3dB attenuator pad between them to reduce interaction.

A sensitive detector

Where signals are large, a simple diode detector and meter will suffice (Fig 6.14). In many instances, a much more sensitive instrument is required, and again the best source is second-hand test gear on sale at rallies and surplus equipment sales. Look out for 'RF millivoltmeters' or 'RF milliwattmeters' – not to be confused with the AF or LF equivalents which are unsuitable for radio frequencies. Sensitive RF millivoltmeters go down to about 1mV full scale, and many of the designs are based on the use of a balanced pair of germanium diodes, followed by a very high-impedance amplifier. The detector/amplifier circuit incorporates range switching and linearising circuits to simplify the scaling of the meter, making quite a sophisticated instrument.

For the amateur who is prepared to use an external switched attenuator and a highly non-linear calibration curve, it is possible to make a sensitive detector using a pair of low-cost germanium diodes, such as OA47s, in a circuit like that of Fig 6.15(a). The operational amplifier must be a high-impedance, FET input type. The only other point to watch is the layout of the diode input circuit. The arrangement of Fig 6.15(b) is recommended. The detector and high-impedance amplifier circuit must be mounted in a metal box with supply leads and output leads (if an external meter is used) suitably decoupled. The attenuator may be a separate unit, in its own screened housing, connected to the detector by coaxial cable. It is important to note that the operation of the detector depends on the particular properties of germanium diodes, and modern silicon diodes are not suitable. A home-made detector of this type can be made to give sensitivities of about 10mV (about 2µW in 50Ω) full-scale deflection with reasonable repeatability, though the zero may need to be re-adjusted occasionally to allow for thermal drift.

A sensitive, untuned detector can be used to make a rough check on harmonics by seeing how much the detector reading is reduced when the notch filter is tuned to the carrier. If the reduction is not over 30dB then something is seriously wrong (Fig 6.11).

Attenuators

Low-power fixed attenuators are simple to construct, providing good RF practice is followed. Resistor values for attenuators will be found in Appendix 5. It is also quite

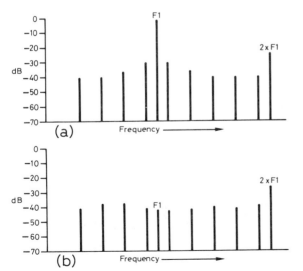

Fig 6.13. (a) Frequency f_1 plus spurious. The analyser will be overloaded by f_1 if gain is increased. (b) Notch tuned to f_1. This reduces f_1 by about 40dB and also adjacent spurious signals to some extent. More remote spurious signals are very little affected. Analyser gain could now be increased without fear of overload to reveal spurious signals which would otherwise be undetected

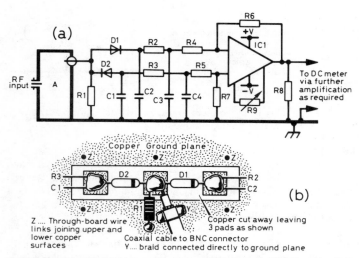

Fig 6.15. (a) A sensitive detector with range selection by switched attenuator. For component values, see Table 6.2. (b) Input circuit – use double-sided board

Table 6.2. Typical component values for Fig 6.15(a)

R1	50R
R2, 3, 8	4k7
R4, 5	4M7
R6, 7	10M
R9	To suit IC1
C1–4	10n ceramic
D1, 2	Germanium diodes (eg OA47)
IC1	FET op-amp (eg TL071)
A	Switchable attenuator (may be separate unit connected by coaxial cable)

Photo 6.2. A home-made low-power attenuator. Two 'islands' are cut in the copper cladding to make pads. If PTFE-insulated coaxial cable is available, soldering to the copper is easy

practical to construct switched attenuators, and information will be found in several amateur publications [8]. In addition, surplus units are fairly common, though many of these will be 75Ω.

High-power attenuators are more of a problem, and it may be difficult to find a suitable one at a reasonable price. One way round this is to make use of the dummy load which is (or should be) part of every amateur station – Fig 6.16 shows the general arrangement. The dummy load forms the first resistor in a pi-attenuator, and R1 and R2 form the other two. Of course, it is impossible to achieve a perfect match because the input impedance will always be less than 50Ω, but in practice, if R1 is made fairly large, the effect is small. A typical value for R1 might be 470Ω, with 56Ω for R2. The two resistors can conveniently be mounted in a small metal box with coaxial connectors at either end. Suitable boxes can be found in electronic component suppliers' catalogues. R1 must be high wattage (roughly one-tenth of the transmitter power in the present example), and it may be convenient to use several resistors in series/parallel. R2 need only be about one-tenth of the wattage of R1, so a 1W resistor will cover most requirements. Both R1 and R2 must be suitable for RF use, which in effect means that they must not be wire-wound and the leads must be kept as short as possible. If high powers are involved, pay particular attention to the construction to ensure that there is adequate clearance to avoid flash-over etc. The attenuation of the unit shown in the figure will be about 25dB, and in most cases it will be followed by a low-power attenuator connected to the output side.

The signal generator

This is not specifically an instrument for EMC investigations, but is essential for calibration and comparison purposes. Signal generators can be home built, and are a very good project for anyone who enjoys the challenge of careful construction. Alternatively there are a large number

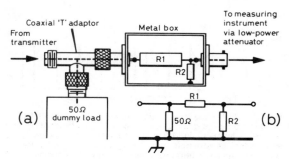

Fig 6.16. (a) The dummy load attenuator. (b) Circuit

Photo 6.3. High-power attenuator (50W, more for short periods) and low-power attenuator (less than 1W). Note the input/output markings on the high-power unit

of generators on the surplus market, ranging from older units dating back to the 'fifties and 'sixties at very reasonable prices, to equipment which is only a few years old and priced accordingly. Most of the older units are of simple design but substantially built, and still capable of good service provided their limitations are understood. In many cases the RF output will be 75Ω (not 50Ω as in modern generators), but in practice this is unlikely to be a major problem in amateur use. It is uncommon to find FM on very old signal generators, though most of them suffer to some extent from incidental FM when the AM facility is in use. Most vintage signal generators use simple valve oscillators, which tend to drift as the unit heats up. This is true of a lot of valve equipment, and can be counteracted by switching on about half an hour or so before starting work so that the temperature has time to stabilise.

The oscilloscope

Again this is not specifically an EMC instrument, but it has become so much a part of the electronics scene that no workshop should be without one. The popularity of the oscilloscope has the advantage that reasonably priced models intended for the non-professional user are available in the electronic suppliers' catalogues. On the other hand, it also means that the chance of picking up a bargain on the surplus market is limited. There are some quite good old oscilloscopes from the valve era to be found on the second-hand market at very low prices but, generally speaking, they are large and heavy. They are only likely to recommend themselves to the amateur who has plenty of space – not to mention some strong friends and a tolerant spouse!

When considering an oscilloscope, look for the maximum frequency which can be displayed. Expensive modern instruments go up to hundreds of megahertz, but a few tens of megahertz is more likely for one in range of the amateur pocket. Some oscilloscopes have a direct input to the 'y' plates and this is a useful feature which permits operation up to much higher frequencies than would be possible through the amplifier, provided a signal of large enough amplitude is available.

An oscilloscope is invaluable in experimental SSB work, for detecting distortion and potential intermodulation problems [9].

Precautions in the amateur workshop

Apart from the usual application of common sense required in any do-it-yourself workshop activity, there are

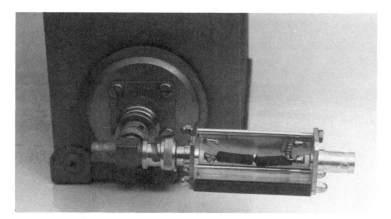

Photo 6.4. Using a dummy load as an attenuator (cover removed to show attenuation resistors). Series resistors are each 220Ω, 2.5W. Shunt resistors are 100Ω and 130Ω in parallel (¼W). Attenuation is 25dB (approx). Will handle up to about 30W and more for short periods. Note that the series resistors will get very hot if the unit is used continuously at powers of more than 10W

a few safety points which are specific to the overhaul of test equipment.

(a) When working on an equipment using valves, remember the high-voltage supplies. If you are not used to valves don't be put off, but DO be very careful. Be very wary indeed of anything with a cathode ray tube – all CRT supplies are dangerous, but some old designs with mains-derived EHT (extra high tension) supplies are positively lethal!

(b) Make sure you always stand on a good insulating surface – not directly on a concrete floor. Avoid shocks between your hands: there is an old saying about keeping one hand in your pocket when working on live equipment [10].

(c) Don't do anything on live equipment except essential measurements, and always use well-insulated probes.

(d) Before plugging a new acquisition into the mains, check the mains plug and power supply wiring, and fit a low-rated mains fuse. Have a look at the condition of any electrolytic capacitors in the power supply. If they are obviously past their best, it may be worth replacing them before going any further. (It is not unknown for electrolytic capacitors to explode, shooting out unpleasant debris with considerable force that could cause injury – particularly to eyes.)

(e) Some older pieces of test gear have the mains supply connected by detachable metal cased connectors which could become live if the wiring is faulty; ideally these should be replaced with a modern connector, or a fixed mains lead.

(f) Check and double check that equipment is disconnected from the mains before carrying out any repairs – this may sound trivial, but it is all too easy to make a mistake in the heat of the faultfinding battle.

(g) Beware of toxic substances. Many of the substances previously used in transformers and capacitors are now known to be highly toxic. Avoid contact with any leaking oils and waxes (use disposable gloves) and dispose of the components and cleaning materials sensibly [11]. A more modern hazard is beryllia (beryllium oxide). This is used in RF power transistors and occasionally in high-power RF attenuators, because it is an insulator with an excellent thermal conductivity. Beryllia is a ceramic material which is safe in normal use, but is very toxic indeed in powder form. Be very wary of anything that looks like broken ceramic.

References

[1] *Radio Communication Handbook*, 5th edn, Chapter 6, RSGB.

[2] 'FET dip oscillator for 1.6 to 215MHz', A L Bailey, *Radio Communication* November 1981.

[3] *VHF/UHF Manual*, 4th edn, Chapter 5, RSGB.

[4] 'Direct digital synthesis', P H Saul, *Radio Communication* December 1990.

[5] 'Technical Topics', *Radio Communication* April 1983.

[6] 'Combination RF wattmeter and parasitic detector', F Brown, *Radio Communication* April 1983.

[7] 'A simple and sensitive field strength meter', J M Noeding, *Radio Communication* September 1981.

[8] *Test Equipment for the Radio Amateur*, 2nd edn, Chapter 9, RSGB.

[9] *ARRL Handbook*, 1989 edn, Chapter 18, ARRL.

[10] 'Technical Topics', *Radio Communication* January 1985.

[11] 'Technical Topics', *Radio Communication* October 1984.

SUMMARY

Predictable spurious emissions

Harmonics

These are multiples of the carrier frequency and are generated by non-linear amplification in the power amplifier or driver stages. Where harmonic generation is causing a problem and the transmitter seems to be operating correctly otherwise, a low-pass filter should be fitted at the output (Fig 4.7).

Spurious emissions caused by the process of carrier generation

If a transmitter suddenly starts to produce excessive spurious emissions, try to find out the frequency or frequencies, and then work out which stage is likely to be producing them. When the stage has been identified, check for:

(a) faults in the filtering, particularly for common ground(0V) impedance, linking input and output;

(b) faults in decoupling circuits;

(c) loose or damaged screening;

(d) faults causing distorted inputs to a mixer;

(e) faults in a mixer circuit itself, particularly where a double-balanced mixer may be operating incorrectly;

(f) tuned circuit filters not tuning correctly.

When aligning a vintage transmitter using the oscillator multiplier technique, be careful not to tune any of the stages to the wrong multiple. This could lead to the transmitter operating on entirely the wrong frequency.

Spurious emissions caused by incorrect transmitter operation

Over-driving an SSB transmitter

This is usually called 'splatter' and is caused by non-linear amplification of the SSB RF signal. The most likely stage to be affected is the power amplifier, particularly if an external linear amplifier is used.

The effect is that the transmission seems to be broad, with unintelligible signals on either side. In the absence of a spectrum analyser, the best way to check is to arrange an organised signal test. The general procedure at the receiving end is as follows.

(a) Arrange receiving antenna conditions so that the signal reaching the receiver is no greater than about S9 – so that there is no chance of receiver overload confusing the report.

(b) Listen carefully to the transmission, tuning on either side of the nominal signal frequency. The signal should fall off very sharply outside the normal speech frequency band. If in doubt as to what to expect, listen to other SSB signals to get the feel of what can be expected from a good transmission.

Avoid splatter by:

(a) ensuring that the automatic level control (ALC) circuits in the transceiver are operating correctly, and that the meter readings are all normal;

(b) keeping the 'mic gain' to a reasonable level, especially if a new microphone is being tried;

(c) checking carefully after making any modifications to signal processing circuits;

(d) when a linear amplifier is in use, making sure that it is driven at the correct level. This is particularly important on field days and similar activities where operators may be unfamiliar with the equipment.

Key clicks

These are caused by switching the transmitter on and off too sharply, generating clicks that can be heard many kilohertz away from the nominal frequency. As with splatter, the best test is to get a report from an experienced amateur. The procedure is pretty much the same, except that the object now is to search for key clicks either side of the nominal frequency.

Unpredictable spurious emissions

Direct instability

This is when an amplifying stage in a transmitter oscillates at, or near, its normal operating frequency. This type of instability shows itself by the presence of RF output when the carrier control is turned to minimum, or more likely by erratic rise of output as the carrier control is advanced. Often the output does not fall as the carrier control is reduced from a high to a low level.

Sometimes a stage will go unstable as the load is changed. For instance, a power amplifier may go unstable when the ATU is adjusted. In general, any erratic behaviour of the RF output should be considered as a possible symptom of instability.

If instability is suspected, check by using a spectrum analyser or a suitable receiver. If an ordinary communications receiver is used, locate it as far away as practical to avoid overloading, and search as widely as possible on either side of the nominal frequency.

Avoid instability by:

(a) following good RF practice when constructing transmitters;

(b) paying particular attention to decoupling and earth return paths;

(c) making sure that screens are really effective. In second-hand equipment check that screens have not been left out or replaced with half the screws missing.

Parasitic oscillations ('parasitics')

These are oscillations which can take place in any part of a transmitter, and can be on any frequency from audio to

(continued)

SUMMARY – CONTINUED

VHF. Parasitics are due to unintentional feedback causing an amplifier to oscillate at some frequency which is determined by accidental resonances. Low-frequency parasitics (and their harmonics) beat with the carrier to give spurious outputs either side of the transmitted signal. High-frequency ones beat with the carrier and its harmonics to give a large number of spurious outputs.

Parasitics can be detected using an analyser or a receiver in the same way as for direct instability.

Parasitic oscillations can occur in any circuit which has gain; modern integrated circuits are particularly prone to unexpected RF oscillation if not correctly used.

Avoid parasitics by:

(a) using good RF technique with proper attention to ground planes etc;

(b) decoupling amplifiers for all frequencies – not just the range the circuit is intended to operate on;

(c) taking care when replacing RF power transistors, particularly if 'near equivalents' are being used;

(d) fitting 'parasitic stoppers' as called for in manufacturers' data and in the design information in amateur radio handbooks.

Chapter 7

Interference to reception

PART 1 – DEALING WITH INTERFERENCE AT SOURCE

Since the beginnings of radio, interference has been a problem. In the far-off days when the Q-codes were devised, transmitted signals were broad and receiver selectivity poor, so that 'QRM' would almost always refer to interference by another signal on or near the same frequency, and 'QRN' would indicate natural static. Over the years, technical advances have changed the picture out of all recognition, and receivers have achieved a standard of performance which would have astounded the early wireless operators. Unfortunately the problem of interference has not lessened – if anything it has got worse.

Today's problems are of two types: the first is simply the overcrowding of the radio spectrum, about which amateurs can do little except to urge the use of good operating practice, coupled with good receiver design [1]. The second is incidental local interference, caused by the proliferation of electrical and electronic equipment. This has been called 'incidental', because it is not caused by a specific communication signal, but is generated as a by-product of some other electrical activity. A great deal can be done to alleviate this type of interference, and the causes and remedies form the subject of this chapter. Unless the contrary is indicated, the term 'interference' is used here to refer to incidental interference.

Interference or static?

For many years the main source of incidental radio interference was impulses of electromagnetic energy caused by rapid discharges at sparking contacts, such as motor commutators or the ignition circuits of motor vehicles. Such discharges were often called 'man-made static' because of their similarity to natural static electrical discharges of thunderstorms etc.

More recently, the simple classification has been blurred by the fact that many sources involve electronic switching, which has characteristics of both impulse and continuous-wave interference. The modern trend is to refer to all such activity simply as 'interference', or sometimes as 'man-made noise'.

Fundamentals

As with any other type of radiation, the emission of interference involves the acceleration of electric charges. Basically, the important factors are the number of charges and how fast they move or, in radio terms, the magnitude and rate of change of current.

The rate at which this energy is released can vary from a short burst of energy from a switched circuit to the continuous output from an oscillator. As a general rule, short impulses generate interference over a wide bandwidth, while the nearer a source approaches a continuous oscillation, the narrower becomes the bandwidth. Underlying this is a fundamental principle which ties together the duration of signals and their bandwidth – in effect you cannot have short pulses and narrow bandwidth.

The rapid release of energy

This occurs when the current in a circuit is switched, either by a mechanical switch or by some form of electronic device, and is usually known as 'impulsive interference'. The radiating circuit will consist of the leads associated with the switched circuit and any other wiring which may be capacitively or inductively coupled to it. A circuit that has been shocked into oscillation will oscillate with an amplitude which decays exponentially and will have fallen to a negligible value after a time equal to about $2Q$ cycles. When a short-duration signal arrives at a narrow-band circuit, such as the IF of a receiver, the short burst of energy is converted into a smaller-amplitude signal spread over a relatively long time (Fig 7.1).

The continuous release of energy

This is where an oscillation is maintained by a supply of external energy – as in almost any oscillator used in radio work. In an ideal case the bandwidth of the oscillation will be negligibly small.

Nowadays the most common sources of interference are digital devices such as computers or games machines,

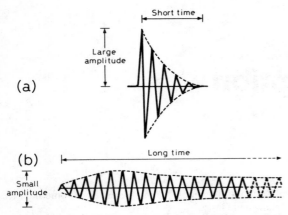

Fig 7.1. (a) Transient energy released in a circuit with a low *Q*. (b) Response of a high-*Q* circuit to a short RF pulse. Amplitude builds up and decays relatively slowly

and these almost always involve a clock oscillator of some sort. The oscillator itself will be a narrow-band source (or rather a series of narrow-band sources, since harmonics will be present), but this will be mixed with a large number of signals generated by switching transients in the myriads of gates in the processor and the input/output circuitry. The result is a broad-band mess, which has the characteristics of transients and of continuous signals, and almost anything in between.

Transferring the energy

The generation of interference is only half the story; equally important is the path by which it arrives at the receiver. The mechanisms by which interference gets out of a piece of equipment are very similar to those by which breakthrough gets in. This is not surprising since the same basic rules of physics apply. The are two ways that interference can find its way out.

(a) *By direct radiation from the point where it is generated.* Generally the conductors inside the offending equipment are short and do not make very good radiators, except where the frequency is relatively high – a wire has to be a significant proportion of a wavelength to make an effective antenna. This means that directly radiated interference is usually more troublesome at frequencies above 30MHz.

(b) *By conduction.* Interference can be conducted to the outside world through any leads which are connected to the equipment. Once outside, the interfering signals can either be radiated or may be carried for considerable distances along the wire. In this case, it is not just a simple case of conduction along a wire; usually the fields are confined between the conductor and earth, forming a crude transmission line. A transmission line of this type will radiate a good deal of the energy supplied to it, so that both conduction and

radiation are taking place at the same time. It is possible for interference to be carried out through the mains supply by the live and neutral cables acting as a transmission line. It is more usual, however, for the signal to travel as a common-mode signal, treating the live and neutral as if they were one conductor, and using earth as the return path. It is also possible for interference to be propagated as a common-mode signal using all three mains wires (live, neutral and earth) as one conductor, and the true earth as the return path.

When considering how radiation takes place from leads coming from the equipment, it is important to remember that the electric charges don't just appear from nowhere. The energy causes the charges to move from one place to another and back again. Very often the two places are an external lead and the capacitance of the equipment to earth. The lead is then acting as a very crude earthed antenna.

Dealing with interference

In most cases it is possible to prevent interference being generated, but usually this will involve some modification or additions to the offending equipment. To avoid constantly repeating dire warnings about the risks of modifying equipment, particularly if it belongs to other people, it will be assumed that two general rules are taken for granted.

1. Don't carry out internal modifications to anything unless you know what you're doing – particularly where safety is concerned. Always play safe.
2. Never attempt internal modifications on equipment which is not your own. Where external modifications such as connecting filters are required, they should be carried out by the owner – helped, where necessary, by the amateur.

Impulsive interference

Where mechanical contacts are concerned, there are a number of well-tried remedies, based on the principle of absorbing the energy which would otherwise be released when the contact is broken. The energy is initially stored in the magnetic field, due to the normal operating current flowing in any inductance which may be present in the circuit, and in many cases this will be considerable. When the contact is broken, the magnetic field collapses and a large voltage appears for a short period as the contacts open, causing a spark. RF currents are exchanged between the inductance and capacitance in the vicinity of the contact, using the ionised air of the spark as a bridge.

The traditional way of absorbing the energy is to connect a resistor and capacitor across the contacts as in Fig 7.2. This effectively 'quenches' the spark by dissipating

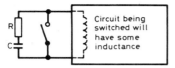

Fig 7.2. A resistor and capacitor used to absorb the energy released when contact is broken

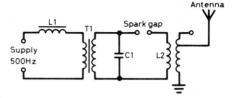

Fig 7.4. A spark transmitter converts low-frequency energy to RF energy

the unwanted energy in the resistor; there is an added advantage of reduced contact wear. The capacitor should be between 0.01 and 0.1μF, and the voltage rating must be several times the voltage being switched. Special capacitors rated for use on AC mains are available, and these must always be used where mains voltages are involved. Devices containing a resistor and capacitor in one encapsulated unit can be purchased from component suppliers. Another approach is to use a semiconductor surge suppression diode or voltage-dependent resistor. It is most important to use the correct type of device and to follow the advice in the manufacturer's data sheet.

Small, low-voltage, DC motors can be suppressed by using a shunt capacitor of between 0.05 and 1μF, and series ferrite-cored chokes of 10 to 30μH, as in Fig 7.3. The chokes are more effective at higher frequencies, and may not be required if only low frequencies are involved. Mains motors are best dealt with by using one of the many mains filters which are available in the suppliers' catalogues. This should be installed as close to the machine as practical.

A very nasty form of impulse interference can be generated at unintentional spark gaps caused by bad connections or by insulation breaking down. The actual mechanism in any particular case is likely to be complicated by the unknown variables which are part and parcel of EMC investigations. A brief diversion into history will highlight the principle.

The spark transmitter (Fig 7.4) operated by converting energy stored in a low-frequency inductance into RF energy. The AC power usually came from a generator at a frequency of about 500Hz, and the effective inductance of inductor L1 and transformer T1 would be more or less resonant with capacitor C1, depending on the design requirements. When the low-frequency energy across C1 reached a sufficient voltage in each cycle, the spark gap would break down, and the energy stored in C1 would then oscillate in the RF circuit, C1 and L2. The oscillatory energy would be coupled to the antenna in the usual way. The similarity to interference generated by sparking at

power transformers or other inductive circuits is obvious. The solution is to correct the fault causing the sparking, though in many cases all the amateur can do is to track down the source and report the problem to the appropriate authority. A similar situation occurs in the cyclic release of short bursts of energy in thyristor control circuits, but in this case the remedy is to fit a suppressor. Suitable devices are readily available from component suppliers, and the correct type should always be used – this is not an area for making do with doubtful components.

Interference from electronic control equipment

In the case of electronic equipment, such as digital control circuits, consider whether it is really necessary to use high-speed logic – lower-speed logic generates less interference because the edges are not so sharp, and also lower-speed devices tend to draw less current, so that the energy involved is less. It may be possible to slow up the edges of a digital signal by minor circuit modifications, but needless to say this can only be done by someone who really understands the implications to the circuit operation.

It is relatively easy to reduce the leakage of interference from a piece of apparatus at the design stage – it is really a matter of good engineering practice. Good decoupling and the provision of a substantial ground plane for the common 0V rail is a good start. The object is to prevent external leads having energy coupled into them from shared return paths, and so acting as antennas (Fig 7.5). Ideally, interference-generating circuits should be completely screened. The screen should be connected to the common 0V point through a path which has the lowest possible impedance. All leads should be decoupled where they pass out through the screen.

In situations where interference reduction is a major factor, for instance where digital control circuits are actually part of the receiver, special attention should be paid to screening, and feedthrough capacitors should be used on all leads. (It is important to choose the correct value. Too large a capacitance will distort fast digital signals.) So far as possible, the screen should be continuous, and where there are any joints there must be good electrical contact along the mating surfaces.

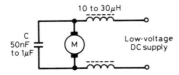

Fig 7.3. Suppressing a small low-voltage DC motor

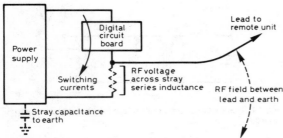

Fig 7.5. External lead, nominally at 0V, acting as unwanted antenna

In most cases of interference to amateur stations, the source will be equipment already installed, where only limited remedial action is possible. There are so many possible situations which could be considered that the easiest course is to pick on one type of installation as an example of the approach to be used. The obvious choice is the home computer and its family of peripheral units, usually known simply as 'peripherals'.

Interference from computer installations

Most interference in computer installations is caused by the external leads and their attached peripherals acting as antennas. These antennas are energised by interference voltages developed across common impedances, generally along the lines illustrated (rather simplisticly) in Fig 7.5. There are a number of variants of this theme, and it is not too much of an exaggeration to say that most interference problems stem from poor 0V rail/grounding practice – either inside or outside the computer. (In this context the terms '0V rail' and 'ground' have the same meaning).

When data signals are passed to a remote part of an installation, such as a printer, the current will go out from the computer on one wire and come back on another. If the wire going out and the one coming back are very close together, as in a twisted pair, the fields due to the outgoing current and the return current almost cancel. As seen from outside, the pair of wires appears to carry negligible current, and radiation is minimal. Computer installations often use ribbon cable to connect peripheral items, and it is good practice to arrange for the signal and return wires to be adjacent to one another. This is not ideal but does give a reasonable degree of field cancellation.

In many installations, particularly relatively low-cost home computers working with non-standard peripheral equipment, the handling of return signals leaves much to be desired. Where several signals share a common 0V return, the impedance of the wire will be common to all the return currents, and the potential across this impedance will cause the 0V rail of the peripheral to be at a different potential from that of the computer. Not only are

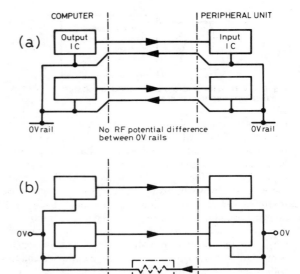

Fig 7.6. Common return impedance causes PD between computer and peripheral unit 0V rails. (a) Individual signal and return lines. (b) Only one return path

the signal and return currents not properly cancelled but, more importantly, interference is injected into the 0V system (Fig 7.6).

The overall effect is that residual (common-mode) currents flow from the computer to the peripheral and then return via any available path. This could be the mains or any stray wiring which may be capacitively coupled to either unit. These currents wandering all over the place will of course radiate interference (Fig 7.7).

Ferrite chokes

The simplest approach is to increase the impedance to common-mode currents by using ferrite chokes, in exactly the same way as described in Chapter 5 for dealing

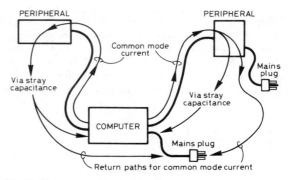

Fig 7.7. Common-mode current paths

with breakthrough. When looking at breakthrough it was convenient to look at the choke as forming the series element of a potential divider; in the present case it is easier to think of the choke raising the impedance of the path, so that the common-mode current is reduced (Fig 7.8).

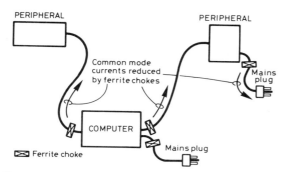

Fig 7.8. Reducing common-mode currents using ferrite chokes

The problem with computer installations is that the cables are usually unsuitable for winding on to ferrite rings. Clamp-up ferrite cores or ferrite rods are a possibility, but neither of these is very practical for use on ribbon cable. It is possible to purchase special clamp-on ferrite devices for ribbon cable, but at most amateur radio frequencies their effectiveness is limited. To achieve a reasonable degree of attenuation, the cable must form several turns on the core. The inductance is directly proportional to the length of ferrite through which the wire passes, and proportional to the square of the number of turns. This means that you get more attenuation by winding several turns on a relatively narrow ring than by using one turn on a thicker ring. (Every time the wire passes through the ring counts as one turn, so a ferrite ring simply slipped on to a wire counts as one turn.)

Screening leads

The adding of ferrite chokes is a relatively straightforward business, and if it does not cure interference completely, at least it is unlikely to make it worse! Screening is more contentious, because it is difficult to apply to an installation which was not originally designed for screened leads. It can be done, but the result will inevitably be something of a compromise.

Where a screened lead is used to connect a peripheral to a computer, the screen has two functions. As might be expected, it does reduce radiation by forming an electrostatic screen around the conductors but, more importantly, it provides a low-impedance path back to the computer for the common-mode currents which would otherwise leak back by devious routes, introducing interference into other units.

Ideally the screen should be good-quality braid, properly terminated in the correct connectors, though in most amateur installations this is likely to be a 'counsel of perfection'. Fortunately, provided the underlying principles are kept in mind, it is possible to achieve good results using low-cost materials and a little ingenuity.

The important thing about screening is not so much the nature of the screen, but where it is connected. It must be taken to a point which is as near as possible at true 0V potential at each end. Many modern computers and peripherals have external metalwork at earth potential or an external 'ground' terminal to which screens can be connected. In such cases there will be no problem finding somewhere to connect the screen. In simpler equipment which has no external metalwork at 0V/ground potential and a two-core mains lead, it must be appreciated that the manufacturer did not anticipate 0V/ground connections being brought out from the case, and this will be reflected in the design of the mains power supply. Think carefully before attempting any modifications, and if in doubt seek expert advice.

Under no circumstances connect anything to the chassis/0V rail of equipment which is not isolated from the mains by a suitable double-wound transformer. In particular remember that domestic TV sets, sometimes used as monitors, often have the chasssis live to earth.

Before going to the trouble of fitting screening, try 'strapping' the 0V rails on the computer and the peripheral together with a short length of braid, about 5mm wide. If this reduces the interference then you are on the right track. Improvements may not be noticeable if other peripherals are still connected. They should be disconnected or similarly 'strapped' to the computer.

In some cases 'strapping' may cure the problem but, if screening is required, there is a choice of using either special screening materials or tapes available from component suppliers, or household aluminium cooking foil. The easiest way to make a contact with an aluminium screen is to include an uninsulated 'drain wire' inside the screen. In effect, wrap the screen over the cable, leaving the 'strap', which we have just been discussing, inside (Fig 7.9).

An improvised ground plane

On the VHF bands it may be found that, even with all the interconnecting cables disconnected, there is still a significant amount of interference radiated directly from the PCB. This is often due to the 0V/ground tracks not having a sufficiently low impedance, so that there is an RF voltage between the 'ground' on one side of the PCB and a 'ground' on the other side. This effect can be reduced by adding a ground plane made of copper-clad circuit board under the PCB as shown in Fig 7.10. The ground plane is single-sided board, rather smaller than the PCB, and

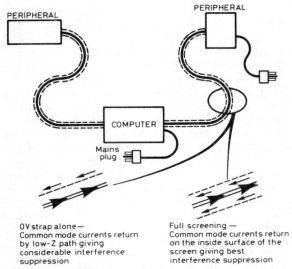

OV strap alone—
Common mode currents return
by low-Z path giving
considerable interference
suppression

Full screening —
Common mode currents return
on the inside surface of the
screen giving best
interference suppression

Fig 7.9. Confining common-mode current by OV rail strapping and screening

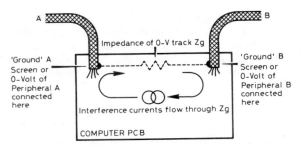

Fig 7.11. Interference currents in the OV track cause the 'ground' connections of the peripherals to be at different RF potential

mounted so that the copper side cannot under any circumstances cause short-circuits.

The new ground plane should be connected to the 0V points on the PCB by short braids – 10 to 20mm if possible. There should be at least four, one at each corner, and where practical one every 50mm or so along the edges. In principle the technique can be applied to any digital PCB, though it is likely to recommend itself to the home constructor rather than to the user of expensive computer equipment. Great care must be taken to connect only 0V tracks, and to avoid short-circuits and consequent damage.

Having established a ground plane, further improvements may be possible by experimentally connecting other 0V points on the PCB to the ground plane. Likewise, the effect of connecting DC supply rails to the ground plane via a 4.7nF capacitor should be tried. Don't forget to switch off and disconnect the equipment from the mains before soldering any straps or capacitors – this may sound obvious, but it is only too easy to forget, as any service engineer will testify!

Any other metalwork in the equipment should be

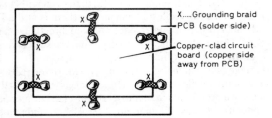

X.....Grounding braid
PCB (solder side)

Copper-clad circuit board (copper side away from PCB)

Fig 7.10. Fitting an improvised ground plane

connected to the ground plane with the shortest possible braid, preferably less than 50mm. Where a computer has built-in disc drives these should be connected to the ground plane by a good RF connection.

Screening the case

Screening the case of a plastic-cased computer is a popular anti-interference measure, but it is by no means always successful. Before committing yourself consider the following.

(a) It is unlikely to effect a significant improvement unless the connections to peripherals have already been dealt with. The analogy about blocking up one hole in a colander has been used before, and applies very much in this situation.

(b) The unsatisfactory 0V conditions on the PCB of the computer, discussed in previous paragraphs, can cause RF voltages to be injected onto peripheral leads, even though the case may be otherwise adequately screened. RF currents flowing in the 0V track cause the two leads to be at different RF potential, as indicated in Fig 7.11, and hence allow interference to be carried out of the enclosure.

(c) The screened case must be connected to the correct 0V point; ideally the ground plane of the computer circuit board. If this is not done, not only will the screening be ineffective, it may even make matters worse. The screen has a large area, and can form quite an effective radiator of any interference which is accidentally fed to it (Fig 7.12).

The most satisfactory method of screening a computer or peripheral with a plastic case is to use a conductive spray paint. These paints are usually nickel based, and are available under various trade names. There are no difficulties in using the spray, providing the maker's instructions are followed, but it is most important to ensure that it only goes where you want it to – short-circuits could be very expensive. If the spray leaves a shiny finish, make sure that the reflection of heat inside the case does not cause overheating. Don't be tempted to block up ventilation holes.

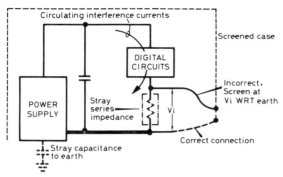

Fig 7.12. Incorrect connection of screened case. Screen is at interference voltage V_i with respect to earth

Mains filters

It is always good practice to include a mains filter in a computer installation. There are a large number of commercial filters available, primarily intended to prevent spikes on the mains from entering the computer. These spikes can be between line and neutral, or between either or both these conductors and mains earth. Filters may consist only of capacitors, whose function is simply to connect the three conductors together so far as RF is concerned. More complicated devices include inductors, sometimes in a balanced arrangement as in Fig 7.13. Most filters do not include any inductance in the mains earth line, but there are some more expensive ones which do. A number of devices also include semiconductor surge suppressors which serve to limit mains spikes.

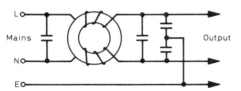

Fig 7.13. Mains filter with balanced inductor (the action of the coil is similar to a very large number of turns of two-core lead on a ferrite ring)

So far as interference is concerned, before rushing out and buying expensive filters for your computer and all your mains-powered peripheral units, consider whether a ferrite ring choke on the mains leads would be adequate. A sensible scheme might be to have one mains filter in the mains supply to the whole installation, mainly to protect the computer from mains spikes, and to isolate the mains leads of peripherals using ferrite chokes. The ferrite chokes are the same as those described in Chapter 5 for the mains leads of susceptible radio and TV equipment. As in that case, where rings are impractical for any reason, ferrite rods can be used. These become more effective as the frequency rises, and at frequencies above

30MHz may actually be superior to rings. The linear winding gives less self-capacitance, and hence improves high-frequency performance.

Connecting a computer installation to a transceiver

As with other aspects of computers, it is impractical to deal with specific cases. Not only are there already a multitude of possible arrangements, but techniques are continually changing, as new ideas are explored.

In this context the transceiver is just another peripheral unit, and the underlying anti-interference procedures are the same.

(a) Try to arrange that all the 0V/ground rails of the various units are at the same RF potential. Where screened leads do not already do this, use short lengths of braid to link together convenient 0V points.

(b) Use ferrite chokes to minimise common-mode currents on inter-unit cables and mains leads.

In addition it is most important to make sure that all received signals come through the antenna feeder, and are not getting in through stray paths in the station wiring.

In extreme cases it is possible to use the cancelling techniques discussed later to reduce interference generated by a computer controlling a transceiver. For the EMC investigator, though, this seems a bit defeatist – rather like a football club that avoids being beaten by getting a carpenter to board up the goal!

PART 2 – DEALING WITH INTERFERENCE AT THE RECEIVER

What can be expected?

At any receiving antenna there is always a background level of noise, natural and man-made, and at HF and low VHF this sets the limit to the detection of weak signals. The intensity of this noise varies with location, frequency and time of day; Fig 7.14 gives some idea of the range of noise levels that can be expected.

At lower frequencies there is a marked difference between daylight and night-time conditions. This is simply a matter of different propagation conditions bringing man-made and natural noise from distant parts of the globe at different times. The natural noise comes from lightning discharges and similar phenomena, which are always taking place somewhere or other in the world. The majority of this interference is impulsive but, as frequencies rise above the HF band, the noise becomes more 'white' and is indistinguishable from front-end noise of the receiver. At these frequencies the noise comes mainly from space, and is usually called 'cosmic noise'. This becomes less as the frequency rises, until above about 100MHz the receiver noise starts to predominate, even with good, low-noise, front-end designs.

Any locally generated interference simply adds to this

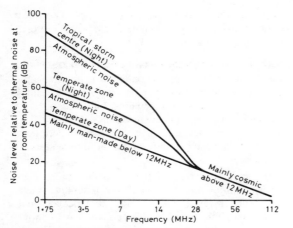

Fig 7.14. Typical background noise levels

background noise which effectively sets the 'bottom line' of interference reduction. It is perhaps worth repeating the well-known fact that there is no point in designing an HF receiver with a noise figure of better than about 10dB, unless it is to be used with a very poor antenna. In all practical cases the external noise will predominate. If you are designing your own HF receiver it a good idea to consider trading off sensitivity for dynamic range; quite a lot of what seems to be interference on HF is actually due to intermodulation in the receiver [1].

Planning a station for minimum interference

Interference reaches the receiver either by direct radiation or by a combination of conduction and radiation. The vicinity of any amateur station will be cluttered by electrical wiring, such as mains supply, telephone or other utilities. There will also be unintentional conductors, in the form of pipes or structural metalwork. This means that interference generated at any particular location is likely to travel at least part of the way by a path involving a conductor of some sort. As previously discussed, signals can travel considerable distances using electrical wiring as a transmission line. In effect the electromagnetic energy is propagated between the wire and earth, though the situation is so indeterminate that it would be unrewarding to attempt to analyse it in any depth. Depending on the conditions, the wiring will also radiate energy; in this aspect the wire usually acts as a grounded antenna. In engineering terms the situation is an untidy collection of unknown factors, but so far as the present problem is concerned the message is simple. Keep your receiving antennas as far away as possible from house wiring.

The rules for minimising interference are the same as for reducing breakthrough (Chapter 3), and the reasons are much the same. Good receiving antennas for the HF bands should be:

(a) horizontally polarised, as interference radiated from house wiring is predominantly vertically polarised;
(b) balanced, because just as poorly balanced antennas give rise to radiation from feeders, they will also allow signals to be picked up by the feeders;
(c) compact, so that neither end comes close to house wiring. Looking at Fig 3.1 (Chapter 3) from the receiving point of view, the electric charges, which are the interference currents flowing in the house wiring, induce equal but opposite charges in the end of the wire close to the house.

On VHF, conditions are different, because at these frequencies the background noise is becoming negligible. In this case the antenna should be as efficient as possible, and should be mounted as high as practical.

The similarity between transmitting and receiving antenna requirements is well known, and there is a general rule in radio engineering that good transmitting antennas make good receiving antennas. Like all good rules this has an exception, at least so far as HF receiving antennas in suburban gardens is concerned. The exception is due to the high level of background noise on the HF bands, which has no effect on transmission but is a very significant factor in reception.

Since, on HF, the minimum receivable signal is determined, not by the receiver sensitivity, but by the ratio between the background noise and the wanted signal, it follows that the efficiency of the antenna is not of primary importance. This means that for reception it may well be worth mounting a relatively inefficient antenna in a good location that gives minimum local interference pick-up.

The active antenna

This is a concept that has been around for some time, but has only become really practical since the advent of modern semiconductor devices with good intermodulation performance. Active antennas can be either balanced or unbalanced but, where interference reduction is the aim rather than simply convenience, a dipole configuration is the best choice. Fig 7.15 shows the outline of an active dipole, along with the equivalent circuit. A typical length for the elements might be between 1 to 2m, which is short compared to a wavelength over the whole of the HF band, and very short indeed at frequencies such as 1.8MHz. By way of illustration, think of a dipole with elements 1m long operating on 10MHz. At this frequency, each element looks like a large capacitive reactance – in the region of 2kΩ – in series with a very small resistance. For the present purpose the resistance can be neglected. If the dipole were connected directly to a 75Ω feeder, nearly all the signal voltage would be dropped across the series

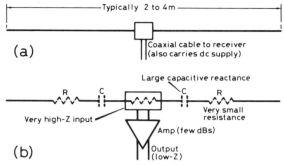

Fig 7.15. An active dipole and equivalent circuit

capacitive reactance and only a very small fraction would appear across the feeder, and hence be fed to the receiver input. In the active antenna the elements are connected to active circuitry which presents a very high impedance to the elements. A second function of the circuit is to amplify the signal voltage developed across this high impedance, and to match it to a low-impedance coaxial feeder.

If the active dipole with 1m elements is receiving signals on 10MHz, the actual signal voltage picked up will be considerably less than that which would be picked up by a full-length half-wave dipole – roughly about a fifth – but looking at the noise levels of Fig 7.14 shows that, in terms of practical signal to background noise, this will have hardly any effect. A dipole of this type is, of course, untuned and will operate satisfactorily over a very wide range of frequencies – typically from medium wave to above 30MHz.

The secret of the design of an active antenna lies in providing these functions without introducing inter-modulation problems, and it is for this reason that active antennas tend to be rather 'thirsty'. Generally good intermodulation performance and high current consumption go together. It is quite practical to build a homebrew active antenna, but achieving the required performance can be tricky. It is advisable to use a published design, at least as a starting point.

There are a number of active antennas on the market, but this is an area where it pays to be careful and to study the specification before committing yourself. The main thing to look for is sensibly quoted intermodulation figures – at least the second- and third-order inter-modulation performance should be quoted. A review of a commercial active antenna suitable for amateur use will be found in [2].

The advantage of the active antenna is that it is compact, and so can be mounted high up and away from local interference sources. If it is to be used with a transceiver, it is essential to ensure that in no circumstances can the transmitted power find its way to the active antenna. This will involve some form of switching by relays, or possibly PIN diodes, and great care is needed to ensure that it is fail-safe.

Interference which gets past the antenna

Before coming to the conclusion that the interference is being picked up in the antenna, check that it is not sneaking in through devious routes. The most obvious is interference coming into the receiver through the mains, possibly as a differential signal between live and neutral, but more likely as a common-mode signal.

The usual check for mains-borne interference is to disconnect the antenna – preferably replacing it with a dummy load – and see if the interference goes away. It is possible for interference to find its way in by routes involving the antenna feeder (or other cables connected to the receiver) acting in conjunction with the mains. Because of this, a better check is to operate the receiver (or another one of similar sensitivity) from batteries and to see if the interference is still present. During the test all associated mains equipment should be disconnected. Many modern receivers or transceivers can be arranged to operate from battery supplies, so this test is much easier than it would have been a few years ago.

If interference is coming in through the mains, the solution is a commercially built mains filter, or a homemade ferrite filter as described previously for combating breakthrough. In some instances interference can be introduced into a receiver by a similar process to that by which it leaks out of a computer: using common-impedance paths. Examine the station layout and ensure that everything associated with the receiver has a common 0V system – in effect this means connecting everything to a common 'earth' point by the shortest possible leads.

Specific action against interference

In some cases, when all the possible good housekeeping measures have been taken, there could still be an intolerable level of interference from some specific local cause. Let us suppose that there is nothing that can be done at the source, and that the only course is to alleviate the interference at the receiving end. For this to be done it is necessary to exploit some difference between the unwanted and the wanted signals, so that one can be reduced without affecting the other too much. There are two possible differences to consider: the first is amplitude, and the second is phase.

Noise limiters and blankers

Noise limiters have been around for decades (since well before the second world war) but the blanker is more complex, and has only become popular with the advent of modern semiconductor receivers. Both techniques are suitable only for alleviating certain types of interference: impulse signals of large amplitude and short duration, such as those from car ignition circuits or similar sources.

The limiter is simply a clipper circuit which chops off the large-amplitude signal at some reasonable level, while letting the wanted signals through unaffected. In traditional designs the limiter comes after the IF amplifier, and this inevitably reduces its effectiveness. By the time the large-amplitude impulse has reached this point it has already been through the IF filter and will have become smaller in amplitude and longer in duration as in Fig 7.1.

The noise blanker also works on impulsive interference, but in this case the large-amplitude, short-duration signal is picked off at an early stage in the amplifier chain before the narrow IF filters. This signal is then amplified, rectified, and used to switch the signals passing to the main receive path. During the short period of the impulse the route to the main path is closed, so that energy from the disturbance is blocked. Since the duration of the impulse (before it is smeared out by the high-Q circuits of the IF amplifier) is very short, the effect on the wanted signal is not noticeable [3].

Interference cancelling

Cancelling is not so well known as limiters or blankers, which is surprising since it is a very powerful technique. It has two big advantages: first, it will work with any type of interference and, second, it does not require any modification to the receiver (or transceiver) itself. For amateur operation, interference cancelling is usually confined to the HF bands, though there is no particular reason why its use should not be extended to 50MHz or higher.

The canceller works by utilising the difference in phase between the wanted signal and the interference. If two receiving antennas are set up some distance apart and the same signal is received on both, then the phase relationship between the currents in the two antennas will depend on the direction from which the signal comes (Fig 7.16(a)). If the two outputs from the antennas are adjusted to be exactly the same in amplitude and exactly 180° out of phase, then if they are added together, they will cancel leaving almost no residual signal. The key to a practical canceller lies in the word 'exactly'; if the phase and amplitudes are not just right, most of the cancelling effect is lost. This is very similar to the loop antenna, or the far more familiar ferrite rod antenna, widely used for direction finding. The null is very sharp, but away from the null the signal strength does not change much (Fig 7.16(b)). In practical amateur reception it is most unusual for two independent signals to have exactly the same null, even if they come from more or less the same direction – on HF most wanted signals arrive at the receiving antenna by a sky-wave path, while the majority of local interference comes along the ground.

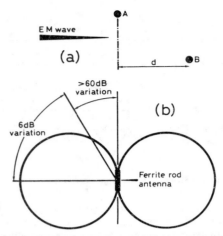

Fig 7.16. (a) An electromagnetic wave arriving at two antennas. The signal at B will be delayed in phase by the time taken for the wave to traverse the distance d. (b) The response of a ferrite-rod antenna. The change of signal strength near the null is large. Away from the null the change is quite small

In an interference canceller the gain and phase of the signals in the two antennas are adjusted, using two control knobs, until the interference is nulled out, leaving the wanted signal more or less unaffected. How much the wanted signal will be affected depends on the relative directions from which the two signals are coming and the distance between the two antennas [4]. As a rule of thumb, for interference coming from a fairly long way off (several wavelengths away), the antenna spacing should not be much less than one quarter-wave at the frequency of operation, though much smaller spacings can be used if some degradation of reception is acceptable. Where the interference source is much closer, the situation becomes very complicated, and it is simpler not to think in terms of antennas and nulls, but of picking up interference to use as a cancelling signal.

The main difficulty in designing a canceller is achieving the required adjustment of phase and amplitude. The latter is a matter of amplification and/or attenuation, which is not too difficult in practice, but the phase adjustment requires some ingenuity. Phase can be varied by using tuned circuits and exploiting the fact that the phase of the circulating currents in a tuned circuit change, relative to the exciting signal, as the circuit is tuned across resonance. A more convenient method is to use an arrangement where a signal is split into two parts, one part being shifted in phase by 90° relative to the other part; the two parts are then recombined. By adjusting the amplitudes of the shifted and unshifted signals, it is possible to achieve any phase shift between zero and 90°. By inverting (changing by 180°) either or both signals, any required phase shift is possible.

A design for a canceller using this principle was

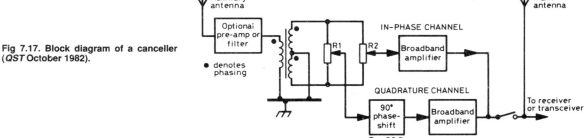

Fig 7.17. Block diagram of a canceller (*QST* October 1982).

published some years ago in *QST* by W1ETC [4]. This circuit illustrates the technique very well, and will form a good basis for experiments with cancelling. The block diagram and circuit are reproduced in Figs 7.17 and 7.18. The 90° phase shift is achieved by using a length of coaxial cable cut to be a quarter-wave at the frequency of interest – not forgetting to allow for the velocity factor of the cable. Fortunately, in practice there is a fair amount of latitude in the cable length so that it is possible to cover more than one band with a particular length. It may be wondered why the relatively high-power amplifiers are used in a receiving circuit; this is an example of using high-power devices to minimise problems from

intermodulation – as mentioned previously in connection with active antennas.

Where the requirement is to eliminate local interference, one of the antennas is usually the main station antenna, and the other (the auxiliary antenna) is a relatively simple arrangement, sited to pick up the interference as well as possible. If more controlled experiments are to be carried out, the wide bandwidth and inherent matching of an active antenna make this a good choice for the auxiliary antenna.

All this talk of exactly adjusting the phase and gain may give the impression that cancellers will only operate in ideal conditions. This is far from the case: in fact they

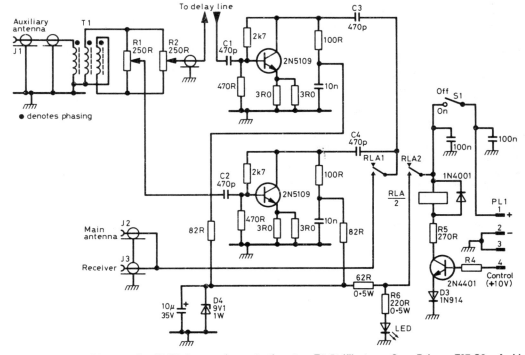

Fig 7.18. Circuit diagram of the canceller. R1/R2: linear carbon potentiometers. T1: 5 trifilar turns. Core: Palomar F37-Q2 or Amidon FT37-63. Note that the circuit around RLA (R5, D3, R4 and the 2N4401 transistor) should be adapted to suit the available relay. The circuit shown is suitable for receive only or for a low-power transceiver. For high power a more substantial relay will be required

will give a good account of themselves in almost all situations – the only requirement is that there must be sufficient amplitude/phase adjustment to cover the range of signal to interference conditions. It is also important to remember that, by its very nature, such a device can only cancel one signal at a time. If the interference is coming from more than one source, or arriving at the station by more than one route, as with ionospheric signals, the cancellation will be limited. In good conditions cancellers can be extremely effective, giving nulls of 60dB or more.

The one type of interference which the canceller will not cope with is natural static. This is because the crashes of natural static come from different locations, so that even if it were possible to cancel one crash, the adjustment

would not be suitable for the next one, and it would get through more or less unaffected.

Commercially manufactured interference cancellers are available, but there is no unanimity about what to call them, so it is important to make sure that the device you are purchasing is what you are looking for.

References

[1] 'Dynamic range, intermodulation and phase noise', P E Chadwick, *Radio Communication* March 1984.
[2] Equipment review, P J Hart, *Radio Communication* June 1982.
[3] *ARRL Handbook*, 1989 edn, ARRL, Chapter 12.
[4] 'Electrical antenna null steering', J Webb, *QST* October 1982.

SUMMARY – DEALING WITH RECEIVED INTERFERENCE

Actions at source
Impulsive interference
(a) Absorb the released energy in some form of 'quenching' circuit (Figs 7.2 and 7.3)
(b) For mains-operated motors and similar devices, fit a mains filter. There are several different designs of filter, so study the manufacturers' literature carefully.

Interference from digital equipment
(a) Avoid common-mode (interference) currents, on leads to external units, by using good 0V/ground practice. Where possible, provide a dedicated 0V return for each outgoing signal.
(b) Reduce common-mode currents by fitting ferrite chokes on external leads (Fig 7.8)
(c) Provide low-impedance return paths for common-mode currents to return to their source, by connecting the 0V rails of peripherals back to the 0V rail of the control unit (Fig 7.9).
(d) Fit screening, where appropriate, but make sure that the screen is connected to the correct 0V point.

(e) Improve the 0V/ground conditions on the circuit board by adding an improvised ground plane (Fig 7.10).
(f) Be careful, and make sure that you know what you are doing. Incorrect connections could be very expensive and, MORE IMPORTANTLY, MAY BE DANGEROUS.

Actions at the receiver
(a) Make sure that the interference is coming through the antenna. Eliminate any pick-up at the receiver or through the mains before proceeding to further measures.
(b) Use a noise limiter or blanker. These are only effective where the interference has impulsive characteristics.
(c) Use interference cancelling. This will work with almost any type of interference. Best results will be achieved where the interference comes from a specific source some distance away. Where cancelling is to be used to eliminate very local interference, it is worthwhile experimenting with the siting of the auxiliary antenna. In many cases a simple wire strung up near the source of interference will be satisfactory.

Chapter 8

The social side

Background

In discussing the technical aspects of EMC, it has been emphasised that the principles underlying EMC problems are relatively simple and predictable. In real life things seem complicated only because of the large number of unknown factors.

A philosophically minded physicist might dispute any claim to absolute predictability, but everyone agrees that at the practical engineering level things are predictable (provided that everything is known about the conditions), even though we may jokingly suspect the operation of that well-known law that states that if things can go wrong, they will, and always at the most inconvenient time.

The social side of EMC problems is quite different; people do not always act in a predictable way. Perhaps this is just as well; it would be a very dull world if we could be sure of how our friends and relations would react on every occasion.

The other person's point of view

How should one deal with a difficult neighbour who is upset because breakthrough is spoiling his favourite TV programme? The response is immediate – there is no specific way, it all depends on the circumstances. A good starting place is to understand the neighbour's point of view. This is not easy, and can be a salutary experience since it involves seeing amateur radio, which we (rightly) see as being something special, through the eyes of someone who sees it as just another hobby.

Two hundred years ago Robert Burns wrote 'To a Louse, On Seeing one on a Lady's Bonnet at Church'. A curious subject for a poem, one might think, and one which gives an interesting sidelight on life in the late 18th century. It contains some very well-known lines which put our problem in a nutshell.

O wad some Pow'r the giftie gie us
To see oursels as others see us!
It wad frae monie a blunder free us
An' foolish notion:

Weighing up the situation

The only way to tackle the personal aspects of EMC complaints is by assuming that the people involved are basically reasonable – even though they may be angry or possibly rude at the outset. Unfortunately this approach will not always work; as we all know, there is a small percentage of people who are just not rational. Before concluding that your neighbours come into this category, consider the following points.

(a) We are all likely to take up strong positions if we have been annoyed by what we consider someone else's thoughtless action. It is a great mistake to let a situation get to the stage of real anger before doing anything about it. Most EMC problems can be solved with reasonable give and take, but once the diplomatic approach has been abandoned the chances are greatly lessened. This applies both ways: if you think you are suffering undue interference from some gadget a neighbour has installed, first make sure of your technical facts and then go and have a word with them. Don't wait until you are really cross about it.

(b) Aggression often masks frustrations which are quite unconnected with the problem in hand. This is a well-known fact of human nature. We all know people for whom nothing is ever right. It is not uncommon for people to go so far as to move house because they can't stand the neighbours, only to find that in a few weeks they are quarrelling with their new neighbours. They may just be unlucky, of course, but the problem may be with themselves. In dealing with neighbours of this type, the best course is to use subtlety; if you can find out what is really upsetting them, it may be possible to improve relations to a point where radio problems are easily dealt with. It is a truism that most people are better for knowing, and you may find that your awkward neighbour is not so bad after all. Even if they turn out to be completely unreasonable you haven't lost anything, and at least you have gained in experience!

(c) Expectation of trouble sometimes causes amateurs to take up a negative attitude to their neighbours, even if no complaints have been received. If you set off with an aggressive, isolationist attitude, then when trouble comes you are not going to have many friends. In an extreme case the awkward person of point (b) might be yourself. Listening to comments on the air and at club meetings it is evident that some amateurs almost take a pride in not knowing their neighbours. The choice is up to the individual, of course, but a friendly smile and a few minutes chat cost nothing and makes dealing with any future EMC problems so much easier.

Dealing with complaints of breakthrough

Let us imagine that a neighbour has come to complain about interference, and that he is quite cross about it. (To avoid having to keep printing 'he or she' all the time, a man has been assumed, though it could just as easily be a woman). As has already been said, the approach in any particular case will depend very much on circumstances, but the following suggestions will at least be a starting point.

Getting off to a good start

(a) Try to keep your temper. If you keep calm and reasonable at this stage it will pay handsome dividends later.
(b) If possible, conduct the discussion sitting down. This helps to make the situation seem more normal.
(c) Explain that most cases of interference are due to breakthrough, but occasionally the amateur station may be at fault. If he cannot give you times and dates which enable you to make a diagnosis, offer to carry out tests (see Chapter 4). If the fault is due to harmonics or other spurious emissions from your station, admit it, apologise, and keep off the offending bands until you have put the trouble right.

If the problem is breakthrough

(a) Tell him about the new regulations. Suggest that the immunity of some domestic equipment still in service leaves much to be desired. Have copies of information sheets, such as the RSGB's *Neighbours' Questions Answered* pamphlet [1] or the DTI's *Advice on Television and Radio Reception* [2], ready to hand so that you can go straight to them.
(b) Ask yourself whether you are practising good radio housekeeping (Chapter 3). If you are doubtful, resolve to do something about it, but keep your thoughts to yourself at this stage.
(c) Offer to help, but make sure that it is understood that this is a goodwill gesture, not an obligation.
(d) Do it as quickly as possible. Nothing impresses a sceptical neighbour so much as being able to fix the trouble in a prompt and business-like way.

(e) Generally it is unwise to offer to pay for filters for other people's equipment – it will almost certainly be interpreted as an admission of guilt. There is no reason why you shouldn't lend ferrite rings or other filters to a friendly neighbour, but remember to ask him to let you have them back when he replaces the susceptible equipment – emphasising the point that the problem is at his end.

Two general points

(a) Don't deliberately run down a neighbour's equipment, whatever you may think. Be positive and talk in terms of modern requirements, and how the new regulations have become necessary. Mention that regulations of this sort have been in force in some countries for a number of years.
(b) If possible, end the interview on a friendly note. Try to bring the conversation round to everyday matters – children, grandchildren, cars, football or anything you can think of which has no connection with radio.

The official path

It is important to make sure that a complainant understands that the 'proper' procedure is to go via the official channels. In the UK this means contacting the Radio Investigation Service of the Department of Trade and Industry. A charge is made for this service and it is the complainant who pays the charge – not the amateur! The reason that this is important is that if it should come to a legal argument it is essential to be able to show that the complainant was in no doubt about the proper procedure and that you did not attempt in any way to mislead him. Having said all this, there is no reason why you should not point out that the majority of cases of interference from amateur stations are due to breakthrough, and that with a little co-operation the problem can, most likely, be solved without the delay and expense of calling on experts to tell him what is general knowledge in amateur radio circles. (If your general knowledge is flagging a bit, revive it by reading Chapters 3, 4 and 5 again!)

If things get out of hand

If things get really bad, don't be provoked into doing anything rash; seek expert help. Most national societies have an organisation for dealing with EMC problems, and will advise their members in cases of difficulty.

In the UK, the RSGB EMC Committee has an EMC helpline for members having serious problems. (For ordinary, non-urgent, problems contact your local EMC co-ordinator). Threats of legal action are not uncommon, but are usually just a ploy without serious intent. If you should receive a solicitor's letter, it is best not to acknowledge it but to contact the EMC Committee via the helpline, or to send a copy of the letter, along with the relevant facts, to the EMC Committee chairman.

The address and telephone numbers for the helpline, the Committee chairman, and the EMC co-ordinators are published in the *RSGB Amateur Radio Call Book* [3], and also from time to time in *Radio Communication*.

Restrictions on operation

If requested or instructed by the authorities to cease operation for a period to give time to investigate the problem, then of course you must comply. Make sure that the period is clearly specified in writing, and that everybody concerned understands that the period is to allow time for investigation and, assuming that the fault does not lie with the amateur, operation will start again at the end of that time. The wise amateur will already have made sure that the fault is not at his end, long before things get to this stage, but it will do no harm to have another look at the station to confirm that all is well and to check the radio housekeeping (Chapter 3).

In extreme cases the authorities may indicate an intention to restrict the power or frequencies used by an amateur station on an indefinite basis ('vary the terms of the licence') even though the interference is not due to a spurious emission from the station (ie it is due to breakthrough). Clearly it is in everyone's interest to avoid this extreme measure – it sets a very bad precedent – and it is vital that the EMC Committee is kept informed as soon as there is any question of a restriction of any kind.

Setting up a new station

There are two main reasons for setting up a station in a new location: moving house, or a brand-new licence. In addition to this, there are always amateurs going back on the air, often after a lapse of many years. Veterans will be only too aware of the pitfalls, but a few suggestions may help newcomers to avoid a serious confrontation.

The first and most important point is to be patient. Don't put up an ugly, 'EMC unfriendly' antenna straight away, and then go on the air on full power 24 hours a day. First read Chapter 3, and then think carefully about your situation. If you think you are likely to have problems, start with an antenna arrangement which minimises the risk of breakthrough, and keep the power down for the first few weeks while you get the feel of the situation. Any complaints which do arise are likely to be fairly mild and easily dealt with without souring relations.

It is a good plan to put up your antenna a few weeks before you actually start operation. The sight of an amateur antenna is often enough to bring complaints of all sorts of interference problems. It is important to make the maximum possible capital out of such situations, which are an ideal opportunity for discussing possible sources of interference, since in this case it cannot be you. Don't lose a golden opportunity by being high handed.

Choosing a house with EMC in mind

Very few of us are in a position to make amateur radio operation a prime factor in chosing a new house; however, in many cases it will be a secondary issue, so that it will be useful to look at a few of the factors involved. From the transmitting point of view, choose a garden shaped so that it is possible to arrange antennas a reasonable distance from your own house and neighbouring houses (Chapter 3). For HF operation, the further away the antennas are, the better; the provision of feeders is a minor problem compared to interference. A nearby block of flats may indicate a potential risk of interference to a cable TV system.

From the reception viewpoint, avoid locations that can be expected to have a high local man-made noise level. At one time this was fairly simple because most noise came from industrial premises, or from electric railways or power lines. Noise still does come from such sources, of course, but nowadays some very nasty noise sources in the form of computer systems and other electronic apparatus can turn up even in the most peaceful residential areas.

Though not strictly an EMC issue, the most important point to check is that there are no restrictions on antennas or other constructions on the property under consideration – other than normal planning permission.

When you are on the receiving end

The boot is now on the other foot, and it is up to the amateur to decide whether the problem is serious enough to warrant doing anything about. All locations suffer from man-made noise to some extent, and minimising its effects is part of good radio housekeeping.

From the official point of view, amateur radio is not a 'protected service', and this means that amateurs do not have a right to protection from interference. Exactly how this is interpreted varies from country to country and administration to administration but, as a general rule, the authorities will not be interested unless the interference affects broadcast radio or television inside the normal service area.

In situations where the interference is strong enough to cause trouble to broadcast reception, then it should be fairly easy to persuade the culprit to do something about it; the real problem arises when interference affects amateur radio but not broadcasting.

Interference from domestic equipment

Very little is likely to be achieved without the co-operation of the owner, and it is in situations like this that being on good terms with your neighbours really counts. Where the source is a computer installation, the point can quite legitimately be made that computers which radiate interference also have poor immunity, and are likely to be subject to unpredictable 'crashes'. Whatever you do, don't imply (even as a joke) that you will deliberately attempt to crash his computer with your RF. This is not only illegal, but would put the whole thing on entirely the wrong footing. It would also be difficult to demonstrate if your bluff were called. Just suggest that poor immunity means that crashes could occur for all sorts of reasons, most of which have nothing to do with radio. This should be enough to interest a serious computer user.

Interference from commercial installations

Sometimes interference is received from computer installations in business premises or public service organisations. The first thing is to find out where the interference is coming from and, if possible, some estimate of the signal strength (Appendix 4). When you are sure of your facts, give some thought to whom you should contact. Generally it is better to contact someone fairly senior in the organisation, but if you are going to contact the head office of a firm it would be courteous to let the local manager know. Unless you are a persuasive talker, it might be better to write rather than telephone. With public services there is usually an officer in each district who deals with communications and he (or she) would be the person to contact. In most cases it should be possible to get their name and the address of their office by ringing the 'enquiries' of the organisation in question. In your letter or telephone call give as much information as possible: frequencies, times, what the signal sounds like etc.

The person you contact may not have a great interest in amateur radio, but he will almost certainly be interested in security. This is the important thing to emphasise. Data leakage can be picked up by unscrupulous people and used for malicious, possibly criminal, purposes. It would not need to be sophisticated hacking – a simple change of signal format might indicate the 'status' of machines or alarms within the premises. Cases have been reported where the information displayed on a computer screen has been picked up and displayed some distance away, simply by decoding the interference radiated. All in all, the firm or organisation would be well advised to keep their signals in their proper place. One very important point: don't try to decode the signal yourself, and don't suggest that you might try. This would almost certainly be illegal; all the amateur should do is to examine the signal to ascertain whether it is an amateur signal or not.

References

[1] *Neighbours' Questions Answered*, an amateur radio information sheet available from the RSGB.
[2] *Advice on Television and Radio Reception*, available on request from the Radiocommunications Agency of the DTI.
[3] *RSGB Amateur Radio Call Book*, RSGB.

Chapter 9

Some specific EMC problems

Interference to telephones

Until the coming of modern semiconductor technology, telephones were straightforward electromechanical devices which rarely suffered from interference, but soon these old stalwarts will have passed into history, to be commemorated only in the late-night TV films. The main problem with modern telephones is breakthrough, caused by rectification and amplification of RF currents. The cure is to avoid the RF getting into the equipment in the first place. There are two courses of action:

(a) first check your radio housekeeping to see that you are not inviting trouble by poor antenna siting;
(b) fit ferrite chokes on the lead to the telephone as close to the instrument as possible. Winding the lead on to a ferrite ring is the most popular method of making a choke, but split-core or rod chokes can also be used. The interference will almost always be common mode, and it is really a question of applying the techniques described in Chapter 5, as is most practical in the circumstance.

Many households have extension telephones connected by plugs and sockets to the 'line jack' provided by the telephone company, and these may involve quite long lengths of interconnecting cable. At the start of the investigation, unplug any extension units and their cable, leaving only the instrument near the line jack connected. Clear any breakthrough on this, and then reconnect the extension leads and telephones one by one, dealing with breakthrough problems as they arise. In some cases it may be necessary to re-route vulnerable extension leads, but in most cases the liberal use of ferrite chokes will prove effective.

In general, it is unwise to attempt to carry out any internal modifications to telephone equipment, even if it is your own property; there are rules about equipment being approved for connection to telephone lines, and most telephone authorities (including those in the UK) do not permit unofficial modifications to anything connected to their lines. If privately purchased telephone equipment is abnormally susceptible to interference, then the supplier should be contacted as discussed under 'Intractable cases' in Chapter 5. In the case of equipment rented from the telephone company or administration, the problem should reported to the appropriate engineering department. There are standard EMC modifications which their technicians will carry out – usually free of charge. Alternatively they may exchange the telephone for a type which has better immunity. Occasionally, breakthrough may be caused by abnormal conditions on the lines before they come into the house. This should be reported to the authority responsible for the lines – but check your radio housekeeping first.

Modern telephones and their ancillary units, such as answering machines, contain logic circuits, often controlled by a microprocessor so that the radiation of clock frequencies is always a possibility. If severe interference is experienced from such a source, the first recourse is to fit ferrite chokes placed as close to the offending equipment as possible, and again split cores and rods can be used where it is not practical to use a ring. If this does not cure the problem the supplier of the equipment should be contacted. Before doing this, it is a good idea to check with your national society to see if the particular item is a known troublemaker, and if so what action has been taken in previous cases. In the UK this should be done through the RSGB's EMC co-ordinator scheme.

Cordless telephones

Those currently in use in the UK operate on a fairly simple duplex system, known officially as the CT1 system. The base station transmits on a frequency around 1.7MHz and receives on a frequency in the region of 47.5MHz, while the handset does the reverse. Only a small number of frequencies are available, reliance being placed on the use of narrow-band frequency modulation (NBFM) to minimise the effects of interference. In practice, the signals received by any base station/handset pair is likely to be larger than signals from other units in neighbouring houses. In an NBFM system the largest signal will capture the channel, effectively eliminating weaker interfering signals. To prevent a particular base station being used by someone else's handset, the pairs of units have a digital access code built in to the control circuitry. Some cordless 'phones do suffer quite severely from hum and other extraneous noises; and it may be necessary move away from specific noise sources when using the handset.

There is obviously a risk of interference from transmitters operating in the 1.8MHz and 50MHz bands, but in fact this does not seem to be a serious problem at the present time. This may be because power on 1.8MHz is limited by the licence requirements, and high-power operation on 50MHz is not all that common. In addition, there is an awareness on the part of the public that the current cordless telephone system is subject to disturbances, and they are prepared to put up with a certain amount of interference.

If trouble is experienced, first check that it is not due to direct breakthrough into the audio circuits. If it is, consider where ferrite chokes can be fitted – as discussed above for an ordinary telephone unit. If interference only occurs when operation on 1.8MHz or 50MHz is taking place, then it is probably due to the transmitted signal getting past the front-end tuning on the cordless telephone. Check the following points.

(a) Is the 1.7MHz wire antenna on the base station arranged to best advantage?
(b) Are the 47MHz whip antennas on the base station and handset properly extended?
(c) Is it possible to resite the base station to provide better communication to the place where the handset is most often used?

There are a number of illegal cordless telephones around, using incorrect frequencies and in some cases using quite high power. If you are suffering interference from one of these, a polite word with the owner is clearly in order.

Satellite and cable TV

Most cases of amateur radio interference to television are due to breakthrough caused by RF currents being picked up by the antenna coaxial feeder and interconnecting leads. In general, satellite and cable TV are no different. Wherever parts of an installation are connected together by long leads, these will act as an unwanted antennas, usually using capacitance to earth to complete the circuit as described in Chapter 5. Fig 9.1 gives an idea of how interfering currents might flow in a typical satellite TV installation. The procedure for combating the unwanted common-mode currents is the same as for any breakthrough situation, but unfortunately satellite and cable TV installations are so variable, and are developing so quickly, that it is not practical to give detailed suggestions. The best thing is to read Chapter 5, and then to decide where best the ferrite chokes can be fitted in the particular installation.

In addition to breakthrough, satellite and cable TV

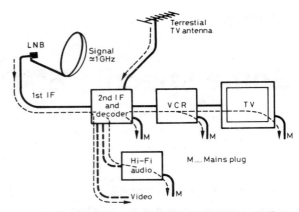

Fig 9.1. A satellite TV receiver installation (dashed lines indicate possible paths for common-mode currents on coaxial braid and other leads)

have their own special problems, involving both received and radiated interference.

Satellite TV

The signal from the satellite is at a frequency in the region of 11GHz, and this is focused by the dish on to the low-noise block (LNB). The LNB contains an RF amplifier, mixer, local oscillator and IF amplifier. The local oscillator is fixed in frequency, using a dielectric resonator oscillator (DRO), which can be compared in function to a crystal oscillator except that it operates at microwave frequencies. This local oscillator beats with the incoming 11GHz signal to generate a first IF output in the range 950 to 1750MHz. (It is probable that this will extend upwards above 2000MHz as the bandwidth of LNBs is increased to accommodate more satellite stations.) The output of the mixer is amplified and passed down a coaxial cable to the indoor part of the installation. Special 'satellite TV grade' coaxial cable with low loss and improved screening should be used to reduce losses and also to minimise the risk of interference from other services. Users of the 1250MHz amateur band will recognise a potential threat here, since this band actually falls inside this first IF band. Fortunately the 1250MHz band involves the use of highly directional antennas, as high up as possible, so that it may be that the problem will not prove as serious as it might at first sight seem. An additional mitigating factor is that satellite TV uses FM with very wide deviation (13MHz upwards, depending on the system), whereas the energy of most amateur signals is confined to a relatively narrow band.

All LNBs are similar in their first IFs, but the handling of the signal in the indoor unit varies considerably and several second IFs are in use. It is unlikely that the nominal frequency of the second IF will fall in an amateur band, but it is important to remember that the IF has a bandwidth of many megahertz to suit the deviation of the system, so that it is quite possible that an amateur band might come within the pass band. It is possible for the harmonic of an amateur transmitter to get into the first or second IF stages, but generally this will not happen unless the harmonic is far larger than it should be.

A variety of encoding and decoding systems are in use by system operators to counter unauthorised reception, and this means that most installations will include some form of decoder. These usually involve high-speed digital signal processing and the consequent risk of radiating interference. In general the causes and cures are similar to those discussed in Chapter 7 with regard to computers.

As with any radio or electronic equipment, a well-installed system is much less likely to give trouble than one which has been thrown together without thought, using the cheapest possible materials. The vulnerable part of all complicated installations is the interconnections, particularly the RF and screened audio or video leads. Make sure that all connectors are correctly fitted and the braid is making good contact. In many cases an installation will appear work satisfactorily even if the braid is not contacting the connector at all. When this happens, the currents which should flow on the inside surface of the braid (in effect balancing the currents on the inner conductor) return by random paths existing between the units. These paths may be through supply cables or through stray capacitance. The net result is that the normal 'go-return' balance which is inherent in coaxial cables is lost, and the stray return paths form a common impedance which 'couples' to the outside world, allowing interference to be radiated and breakthrough to find its way into the system (Fig 9.2).

Cable TV

This has come into prominence in recent years as more complex systems, often operating in conjunction with satellite TV, have come into use. Actually cable TV has been around for decades and many blocks of flats have been fitted with cable TV outlets fed from a single antenna and amplifier. These systems have been a thorn in the flesh of many amateurs over the years. Problems occur when the amateur signal gets into the antenna amplifier unit, causing overloading and consequent cross-modulation. The resulting interference affects every TV set in the block, and needless to say generates a great deal of ill-feeling.

There are really only three practical actions that the amateur can take.

(a) Make sure that the trouble is definitely not due to transmitter defects – harmonics or other spurious emissions as dealt with in Chapter 6. In this situation it is well worth while spending time and effort in making sure of this point. Not only will it make you

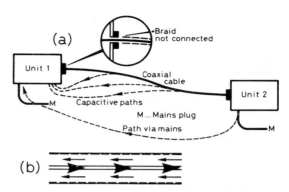

Fig 9.2. (a) Broken braid connection cause the currents which would normally flow on the inner surface of the braid to return by random paths. (b) In a correctly connected coaxial cable the currents balance, giving no external field

feel confident in any discussions, but finding your own problems early will save you being embarrassed later on.

(b) Ask yourself (and give yourself honest answers) whether you are practising good radio housekeeping (Chapter 3).

(c) Advise complainants that the interference is due to a defect in the cable TV installation and suggest that they contact the organisation managing the flats. Explain that there is nothing you can do at your end to prevent the interference, but that you are willing to co-operate in any tests which may be required.

Large-scale cable TV systems covering whole towns are relatively new in the UK, and a variety of systems are under consideration in different locations. One system involves distribution by coaxial cable with carrier frequencies in the VHF band. Where many channels are to be supplied, the cable carries signals covering more or less the whole VHF spectrum. This means that there could be signals in the cable on the 70MHz band and the 144MHz band.

There are two risks: first, that signals will leak out of the cable and cause interference to the amateur bands, and, second, that amateur signals will find their way into the cable and cause interference to users of the TV channels which fall on those frequencies. The usual cause of both problems is some sort of discontinuity in the braid of the coaxial cable; the most common place for this to happen is at junctions or connectors. The mechanism is generally similar to Fig 9.2 except that the common-impedance leakage paths would be much longer. In most cases there will not be much that the individual can do, except to trace the location of the leakage as far as possible and then to report it to the appropriate authority. There are limits to the maximum permissible leakage from a cable system but, as with most emission regulations, they are framed round large-signal reception so that interference could still be experienced on amateur bands even if the regulations are complied with.

Mobile operation

So far as amateur radio is concerned, 'mobile' almost always means some form of motor transport, and in this case it has been assumed that the vehicle is a car, though it could just as well be any other form of motor transport – the problems will be basically the same.

There are two ways in which EMC factors affect mobile operation:

(a) interference to reception caused by electromagnetic energy generated in the engine and ancillaries;
(b) interference by radio transmitters to electronic systems controlling the engine and ancillaries.

The first of these is as old as mobile radio itself. Leafing through old copies of amateur journals will turn up articles on interference suppression going back to the days when 160m was the popular mobile band – and a mobile antenna really added something to a car! These traditional sources of interference are well known, and suppression techniques are covered in other handbooks [1]. In recent years this type of interference has become less important for a number of reasons. One is that nowadays many cars have a broadcast radio fitted as standard, so that at least basic interference suppression is built in. Another factor is that the majority of amateur mobile communication now takes place on VHF FM, which is inherently less susceptible to impulsive interference than SSB or AM. The immunity of an FM receiver to impulses (or any other AM signal) is due to the action of the limiter. Sets vary in the degree of limiting designed into the system. If a particular radio seems to suffer unduly from interference, suspect a lack of signal at the limiter, caused by a fault or a design weakness.

On SSB and AM the effect of impulsive interference can be greatly reduced by the use of a good noise blanker. A blanker operates by using the very short impulses of interference to operate a gate in the receiver IF as described in Chapter 7, and its performance is dependent on a number of factors, including the ability of the receiver front-end to handle large impulses. In practice the effectiveness of blankers varies considerably, so it is worthwhile trying the noise blanker in a practical test before deciding on a transceiver for mobile use.

RF interference to electronic control systems has become a major factor in mobile radio; not least because the possible safety aspects attract publicity. Basically, the problem is caused by RF energy being picked up in the wiring of the car and entering the logic of the control circuits. The effects can vary from specific faults, such as failure of door locks or erratic flashers [2], to complete failure of the microprocessor engine control. Fortunately (from the amateur's point of view) the increasing use of mobile transceivers for leisure and commercial purposes has meant that EMC is becoming an important feature of vehicle design. The biggest problem is HF operation, where the cable harnesses can form quite efficient antennas.

When considering a mobile HF station it should be borne in mind that high-power HF operation may not be practical in any particular car. It is also worth sparing a thought as to whether it is wise to be so close to antennas radiating high powers. Of course it can be argued that the car more or less forms a metal box, but it would be a rash to attempt to be so dogmatic in so complex a situation. All in all, this is probably another case where moderation will pay dividends. Keeping the power down to reasonable levels – perhaps 25W mean power – on both HF and VHF would seem a sensible compromise.

The various metal assemblies in a car may not be in good RF contact, and bonding various parts can result in a reduction of received noise and in improved immunity. Be careful of course, and don't be fooled into thinking that 12V is safe. Short-circuits can cause nasty burns, and bursting batteries are not unknown. At worst you might set fire to the car which will solve the interference problem in a way you hadn't bargained for!

Co-locating transceivers

Operating transmitters and receivers in close proximity has always been a problem, but it has come into prominence in the last few decades as radio systems have become more complex. The design of co-located radio systems is a special branch of radio engineering, and the satisfactory operation of so many amateur repeaters bears witness to how well the principles can be made to work in practice. There is plenty of information around on co-location for VHF and UHF systems, both amateur and commercial [3], and we will confine our discussion to 'unengineered' situations where it is a case of making the best of what is available, rather than designing the system to suit.

A practical example might be a special-event station where it is desired to operate two HF transceivers (on several HF bands) and one transceiver on each of the 144 and 432MHz bands.

Fundamentals

The unwanted interaction between co-located transceivers is just another case of interference, and falls into the two main categories: unwanted emissions by the transmitter and unwanted reception by the receiver. Where modern, well-designed equipment is being used, most of the problems will stem from various sorts of unwanted reception – generally breakthrough, due simply to the fact that very large signals are being radiated close to antennas which are being used for reception on another band. There will of course be spurious emissions, whatever transmitter is being used, but these are unlikely to fall into the amateur bands, and if they do it is usually possible to avoid the frequencies which are affected. The one serious exception to this is harmonics. There is really no chance of being able to reduce harmonics to a level where they will not cause trouble, and the only solution is to plan the station to avoid one transceiver operating on the harmonic of another. In practice this means co-operation between the operators of the various transceivers.

A much more important problem is overloading of receivers by large signals. All receivers have spurious responses, and the reduction of them is a major factor in modern receiver design. Reviews of transceivers in amateur journals devote considerable space to discussion of the large-signal performance. A typical example is [4]. In most cases it will be a question of using available equipment, but if there is any choice then it is obviously best to choose a transceiver with a known good large-signal performance.

The whole strategy of co-location is to reduce the amount of unwanted signal getting into the transceivers, and this is really a matter of planning and good radio housekeeping.

Guidelines for HF operation

(a) Plan the frequencies and antennas so that everyone concerned is quite clear which antennas are to be used on which frequencies. Think of the antennas that are to be used simultaneously as being in different groups. A simple arrangement would be to have a low-frequency group and a high-frequency group. Keep the antennas in different groups as far apart as possible. Low-frequency antennas should be arranged to be the most distant since feeder losses will be less. Minimise losses by ensuring that the distant antennas are well matched [1]. For a 3.5 or 7MHz dipole with a VSWR of less than about 2:1, 100m of UR67 or RG213/U would be quite reasonable. Where long feeder lengths are used, don't forget to check the VSWR at the antenna end of the feeder, otherwise very misleading results can be obtained.

(b) Avoid antennas which use earth as part of the antenna system – practically this means avoiding antennas tuned against ground.

(c) Use balanced antennas, and choose antennas which do not have normal resonance in the other group of frequencies. A dipole is a good choice, but don't forget that a 7MHz dipole has a resonance at 21MHz.

(d) Try to avoid antennas in the different groups running parallel to one another.

(e) Pay particular attention to feeders. In many cases coaxial feeder with a balun at the antenna end is a convenient arrangement. Where the station layout

permits, a non-resonant dipole with tuned feeder can be used [1]. In temporary locations, 300Ω ribbon is simpler to use than open-wire feeder, but if possible the type with slots cut away in the insulation should be used. This type of antenna and feeder may seem a strange choice, but it has the advantage that it can be made to have a fairly high Q, and so helps to increase the isolation of the transceiver at unwanted frequencies.

(f) Always use a manual ATU with each transceiver, even if the antenna in use does not need one to achieve a match. An ATU will help to increase the isolation, but more importantly a manual ATU will also reduce the chance of two transceivers attempting to operate on the same band. This point is most important. Serious damage could be done to a transceiver if it is switched to the same band as a transmitter and the antennas are close together. This is a special risk with modern semiconductor equipment: not only are semiconductor devices more vulnerable, but the ability to switch from band to band at the press of a button makes accidents more likely.

Guidelines for VHF operation

(a) Keep the VHF and UHF antennas as far away as possible from each other and from the HF antennas.

(b) Plan operation to avoid third harmonics from the 144MHz band causing trouble at 432MHz.

(c) If band-pass filters are available, they will greatly increase the isolation.

(d) Use dedicated VHF and UHF transceivers, well designed and well screened. Transverters are almost certain to give problems when co-located with HF equipment.

(e) It is quite possible that HF signals may be picked up on the antenna coaxial cable of VHF equipment, causing a classical breakthrough problem. A ferrite ring choke fitted to the cable near to the transceiver should reduce the unwanted signals, but if not a ferrite choke in the mains lead can be tried. If the trouble persists, then the station layout should be reconsidered, and possibly changes made to the HF antenna or feeder arrangements.

Make sure that all RF connectors are correctly fitted, and that they are fully mated. Passive intermodulation products (PIPs) can cause unexpected interference problems where several transceivers are co-located, and care should be taken to ensure that all connections and antenna fixings are clean, tight and free from corrosion. Use ferrite ring chokes on ancillary leads and microphone cables to reduce unwanted RF currents.

When operating co-located transceivers, moderation pays handsome dividends. Don't be tempted to run excessive power, particularly on the HF bands, and keep the microphone gain on all the transceivers at a reasonable level to avoid overdriving and consequent splatter.

References

[1] *Radio Communication Handbook*, 5th edn, RSGB.

[2] 'EMC Matters', *Radio Communication* December 1991.

[3] *The ARRL Antenna Book*, 16th edn, ARRL, Chapter 17.

[4] 'The Peter Hart Review', *Radio Communication* October 1991.

Appendix 1

Protective multiple earthing (PME)

'Safety in the shack' is the RSGB's general warning statement on PME and amateur radio. Like most general statements, it requires some interpretation to cover any particular situation. The rest of this appendix is a guide to assessing the risks and deciding on a course of action, but it must be emphasised that, when in doubt, the advice of the local electricity supply authority should be sought.

Safety in the shack

Protective multiple earthing (PME) is concerned with the incoming mains supply and the earthing of the mains and the radio equipment.

In a PME system, the main earthing terminal of an installation is connected to the neutral of the electricity service. All metallic surfaces within the building, including gas pipes, water pipes, central heating systems and accessible structural steelwork are bonded together at the consumer unit. This gives the consumer an earth of very high reliability and of low impedance. Under normal circumstances a small voltage may appear between a PME earth and the true earth potential measured outside the building as a result of voltage drop in the neutral of the electricity supply company's system. Under very rare fault conditions, such as a rupture of the neutral conductor on the supply company's system, a higher potential difference may appear which could in theory rise to phase-to-neutral voltage (240V). Because all the metalwork in the building is bonded together, the shock hazard is minimised as the premises are effectively a Faraday cage.

It is permissible to connect other means of earthing to the main earthing terminal of the installation. However, where a low-impedance RF earth is connected directly to radio equipment, a very large current could flow down the earth wire in the power cable of a transmitter, receiver or transceiver in the unlikely event of rupture of the neutral. This current could be as high as several tens of amps. After consultation with the Electricity Council, the Technical & Publications Committee of the RSGB offers the following advice to members whose properties have a PME earthing facility.

1. Disconnect the equipment from the mains, and install an RCD (residual current device). Typical RCDs are available from RS Electromail as RS334-094 to fit on the cable or the wall socket, may be replaced by RS331-095 or 331-102. Now disconnect the earth wire in the 13A plugs and loop it back outside the plug so that it cannot flap around. Attach a label to the plug saying 'NOT EARTHED'. Connect the chassis of each piece of equipment to the radio earth, using a conductor of at least 7/1.35mm, and place a label on the earth lead at each piece of equipment saying 'SAFETY EARTH – DO NOT REMOVE'.

   No metalwork bonded to the main earthing terminal in the consumer unit is then allowed within two metres (six feet) of the radio equipment. This includes radiators and portable electrical equipment such as electric fires, kettles etc, not connected to the RF earth. The use of the RCCB is mandatory.

   The RF earth should be as low a resistance as possible for 50Hz; although this will generally be the case, connections to earth must be of a suitably generous-sized conductor, eg 32/0.2mm, and comply with the IEE wiring regulations requirements for protective conductors. Particular attention may be required where a screened earth lead is used.

2. If the 2m separation is impossible, the RF earth should be bonded to the PME bonding point at the consumer unit. Under these circumstances, the earth conductor must be at least 10mm² (7/1.35mm), and preferably larger. All parts of the RF earth (eg radials on vertical antennas) must be of suitably heavy conductors, in order to ensure that mechanical damage to the earth system will not lead to excessive current density in one or two conductors in the event of a fault. RF isolation between the earths should be provided by winding the lead to the RF earth round ferrite rings. Because of the conductor size, and resulting inflexibility, it is recommended that not more than four turns are used, and therefore a minimum of five and preferably eight rings are used, stacked together. Suitable rings are available from RSGB HQ. The radio equipment should

be connected to the RF earth, and NOT to the supply earth at the wall socket.

3. Where, for EMC purposes, it becomes necessary to provide an RF earth on ANY equipment (eg electronic organs, hi-fi amplifiers etc), the above precautions MUST be followed. This is to meet safety requirements, and not just for EMC purposes. Remember that installing RF earths in a neighbour's house which do not meet these recommendations could leave you in a very perilous situation resulting in fire, injury or death!

4. It is not necessary for an installation to have PME, and if you wish to have the PME removed, this may be done. However, it MUST be done by a suitably qualified person, and you should get professional advice as it will be necessary to fit an RCD at the consumer unit, as well as providing suitable earthing.

NOTE: PME systems started to be installed on a wide scale in the mid-'seventies. If your house is more modern than this, it is highly likely that you have a PME, and you should take appropriate action. If in doubt, your local electricity supply company should be able to tell you.

The risks of PME

(a) In PME systems the supply authorities take great care to ensure that supply faults, such as ruptured neutrals, do not occur, and that if they do, the risk of serious accident is minimal. In practice, serious accidents due to supply faults on PME systems are very rare – so rare that there are no real cases to discuss, and the following notes are based on purely hypothetical considerations. The fact that the risk is insignificant is, however, dependent on sensible precautions being taken where an installation is non-standard – for instance, if an RF earth is being used for a radio station.

(b) The risks from a PME installation stem from the possibility of a ruptured neutral in the supply to the consumer's premises. The break in the neutral could occur anywhere in the supply, and could affect just one house or several houses, depending on the supply arrangements. This could cause the neutral, and the mains earth which is bonded to it, to rise above the 'true' earth potential. To avoid the possibility of metalwork inside the house being at a different potential from the mains earth (which in this case is at neutral potential), the IEE regulations state that all metalwork such as central heating systems, water pipes, gas pipes etc should be securely bonded to the neutral at the PME bonding point near the consumer unit, as in Fig A1.1. In the unlikely event of a ruptured supply neutral, the current which would normally return via the neutral will attempt to return by way of

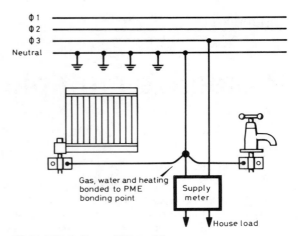

Fig A1.1. Protective multiple earthing

all the other earthed conductors – including the RF earth to amateur radio equipment (Fig A1.2).

(c) In many households there will be conductors which are bonded inside the house to the PME bonding point; which pass out though the walls to the outside of the house; and which could become live with respect to the true earth, should a ruptured neutral occur. An obvious example is an outside tap. It seems reasonable to assume that, in practice, in a properly installed PME system, the 'outside tap' situation is not a significant risk. It cannot be seriously supposed that the authorities would permit a system in which something as readily accessible to children as a garden tap could constitute a real danger.

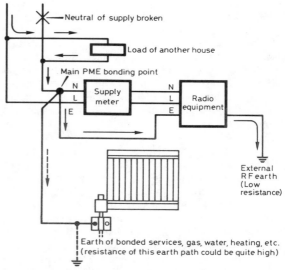

Fig A1.2. A ruptured supply neutral could cause a large current to flow in a low-resistance RF earth

(d) If a ruptured neutral were to cause a significant voltage to exist between the neutral/mains earth and the true earth, then the existence of a fault will be revealed by the drop in the supply voltage between live and neutral. In other words, the mains voltage will have dropped, the loss being roughly the same as the voltage between the neutral/mains earth and the true earth. This is doubtless another reason why accidents are very rare – any faults on the supply are likely to be reported and corrected very quickly.

How PME affects the radio amateur

(a) If an RF earth connection is brought into the house and connected to the metalwork of equipment which is otherwise earth-free, a hazard is created, because under the supposed supply fault conditions a voltage could exist between metal connected to the RF earth and the other metalwork inside the house which is bonded to the supply neutral.

(b) If an RF earth is connected to apparatus which is itself earthed to the mains earth system, then in the case of the supposed fault, very large currents (eg several tens of amps) could flow through the mains earth system and down the RF earth lead, giving rise to a fire risk.

(c) For these reasons there is a general requirement that any external earth (in our case the RF earth) should be bonded to the PME bonding point using a conductor of not less than 10mm^2. This prevents a significant difference in potential existing, and also provides an adequate path for prospective fault currents.

(d) In amateur stations which do not use an RF earth, antennas which are effectively connected to the equipment metalwork, and thence to the mains neutral/earth, represent an 'outside tap' situation as discussed above and are presumably acceptable for the reasons stated. However, it is obvious commonsense to keep the facts in mind when mounting antennas, and when considering arrangements for disconnecting the station from the mains when not in use.

The options

It will be almost impossible to guarantee the 2m separation called for in solution 1 of 'Safety in the shack' above, unless the station is housed in a separate room dedicated to the amateur station. Unfortunately most of us are not in this happy position!

If it is practical and desirable to have the PME removed, then this will immediately solve the problem; but again this is a solution which will not be available to many amateurs, and may bring other technical and safety problems of its own. It is most important to remember that work of this sort must be carried out by a properly

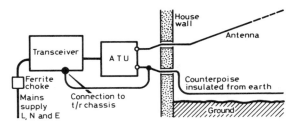

Fig A1.3. Antenna and counterpoise with no external earth connection

qualified person. It must certainly not be considered as a DIY activity under any circumstances.

For most amateurs, bonding the RF earth to the PME bonding point will be the preferred solution. This should be carried out using a conductor of 10mm^2 or greater. To keep the RF currents out of the mains earth, a ferrite choke is formed by winding this conductor on a stack of ferrite cores – as described in 'Safety in the shack' above and in more detail in [1].

Difficult situations

Where it is difficult to get to the PME bonding point, there are several options, depending on what type of amateur station is being considered.

(a) If the installation involves metal towers or masts etc which are earthed by their normal construction, there seems to be no alternative to bonding the RF earth and tower/mast metalwork to the PME bonding point as discussed above. Fortunately anyone who has such an installation in the garden is likely to be one of the householders – or at least to be on good terms with them – and so to be in a position to do the necessary wiring work.

(b) For simple installations it is possible to make an antenna system that has no DC or low-frequency connection to any outside earths. As discussed above, this resembles the 'outside tap' situation and is presumably acceptable. Where an inductively coupled antenna tuning unit (ATU) is used to couple a single-ended antenna and counterpoise, as in Fig A1.3, there must be a DC connection to the transceiver chassis so that the antenna is connected to the mains earth system. This prevents the chance of a shock under the supposed supply fault condition, should the antenna have a (high-resistance) leakage to earth. (There is no risk of large currents flowing, but quite a small leakage current could give a serious electric shock.) With the balanced system of Fig A1.4 it should be possible to ensure that the leakage resistance of the antenna to earth is very high (greater than 100kΩ for instance), but if there is any doubt then some form of DC connection to the transceiver chassis should be provided.

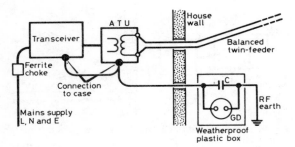

Fig A1.4. Balanced antenna – inductively coupled ATU with capacitively isolated EMC earth. GD: gas discharge device. C: Class Y ceramic capacitor

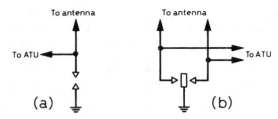

Fig A1.5. Using spark gaps or gas discharge device to give lightning protection. (a) Single-wire antenna. (b) Balanced feeder

On VHF it is quite common to operate without an RF earth, and it is quite possible to do so on HF provided that due consideration is given to EMC aspects. The arrangement of Fig A1.3 is quite suitable for low-power operation, but is not recommended for high power, partly because it is an 'EMC unfriendly' antenna (Chapter 3), and also because the counterpoise could have very high RF voltages on it which is generally undesirable, even if it is well insulated by mains voltage standards.

(c) Where an RF earth is required for EMC purposes in an antenna system which is otherwise earth-free, it may be possible to use an RF earth which is isolated by a capacitor so far as mains frequencies are concerned. Obviously the capacitor must have a low RF impedance, which means a value of about 0.01μF and a suitable voltage rating. The traditional solution would have been a moulded mica capacitor with a (DC) voltage rating in excess of 1000V, but unfortunately these components are now very hard to acquire – at least at a practical amateur price. In recent years, Class Y ceramic interference suppression capacitors have become available and it seems likely that these would be satisfactory. ('Class Y' means that the capacitor is approved for use at mains voltages, in circumstances where failure of the capacitor could result in someone getting a shock – in other words they will withstand mains voltages safely.) A capacitor-isolated earth of this type cannot be used where the RF earth carries the actual antenna current (Chapter 3); it is strictly an EMC earth for systems which are nominally balanced, but require a low-impedance path for residual out-of-balance currents etc. Fig A1.4 shows a typical arrangement. The gas-discharge device [2] is included to give a degree of protection against surges.

The capacitor and discharge device should be housed in an insulated (plastic) box, and installed in a completely weatherproof location. Mount the capacitor and discharge device as if they were actually at mains voltage – the whole point about fitting them is that they could become 'live' on one side, should a supply fault occur.

Lightning protection in a PME system

Lightning protection is not covered in this manual, but general information will be found in references [2], [3] and [4]. If the RF earth is correctly bonded to the PME bonding point, then the installation can be treated as if it were a normal, non-PME, installation.

Where the antennas are earth-free and a counterpoise or a capacitor-isolated RF earth is in use, then we have the problem of providing lightning protection without actually connecting the earth to the antenna system. This requirement can be met by using spark gaps, or gas-discharge devices [2], as indicated in Fig A1.5. Information on making suitable spark gaps can be found in references [5] and [6]. In a PME installation the spark gaps should be mounted and protected as if mains voltages were involved; under the supposed supply fault conditions this might be the case. If it is desired to connect such an antenna system directly to earth when, for instance, the station is out of use for an extended period, this should be done by disconnecting the feeders outside the house and connecting them directly to a low-resistance earth. There should be no other connection to this earth.

References

[1] 'Talking Point – Safety in the shack', *Radio Communication* February 1987.
[2] 'Lightning and EMP protection of amateur radio equipment', G R Jessop, *Radio Communication* December 1982.
[3] 'Lightning', A Martindale, *Radio Communication* January 1984.
[4] BS6651 – Code of Practice for Protection of Structures against Lightning.
[5] *Radio Communication Handbook*, 5th edn, RSGB, Chapter 19.
[6] *ARRL Antenna Handbook*, 14th edn, ARRL, Chapter 8.

Acknowledgement

The author wishes to acknowledge the assistance of the Electricity Association in the preparation of this appendix.

The Association was supplied a copy of the appendix, and asked to contribute a statement on the aspects which come within its province. It was good enough to supply the following:

"The Electricity Association, which is responsible for publication of *Engineering Recommendation G12/2 –* *National Code of Practice on the Application of PME to Low Voltage Networks*, agrees with the references in the appendix which are particular to mains supply and the provision of earthing facilities from PME systems. Regional electricity supply companies (RECs) publish their own guides on the connection and use of PME earthing facilities and these should be consulted by consumers."

Simple Spectrum Analyser

For most people, a spectrum analyser is way out of reach – but this design by Roger Blackwell, G4PMK, which first appeared in Radio Communication *November 1989, makes a homebrew unit a real possibility.*

The Simple Spectrum Analyser (SSA) offers reasonable performance over the range 1–90MHz or so, is cheap to build, and utilises almost any oscilloscope as its display. It has selectable, calibrated, frequency sweep-width ranges, accurate logarithmic signal strength calibration, a dynamic range of over 50dB and a built-in frequency marker generator.

Origins

The original idea for the SSA came from an article by Al Helfrick, K2BLA, who described a basic analyser using only three chips [1]. I have added some features contained in an earlier design of his [2], plus some of my own, based upon a prototype which has now been in use for over a year. Following a certain amount of correspondence [3], and a good deal of information in *Technical Topics* concerning the 'BLA design [4, 5], there was such an overwhelming response, over 120 enquiries, to my offer of further information and numerous requests for PCB layouts, that I decided to write up the project in more detail. The design presented here was developed with home construction in mind and therefore uses pre-wound coils and PCB designs which will hopefully ensure fuss-free construction.

Suitable oscilloscopes for use with the SSA will have a DC-coupled Y amplifier offering 100mV/cm sensitivity and an external input to the X amplifier. In practice the majority of modern general-purpose oscilloscopes will be suitable.

Spectrum analyser operation

Before looking at the circuit in detail, it is worth reviewing the purpose of a spectrum analyser and how it operates. Essentially, it is no more than an electronically tunable receiver, the S-meter output of which is connected to the Y input of an oscilloscope.

If a sawtooth waveform is connected to the tuning line of the receiver VCO and also to the X input of the oscilloscope, a display of frequency against signal amplitude is obtained over the tuning range of the receiver. If the receiver also has a logarithmic response to input level, then relative signal strengths can be read off the screen. A typical display is shown in Fig A2.1.

Of course, life is just a bit more complicated than that and, just as with real receivers, spurious response, selectivity and overload problems occur. The overload problems can be eliminated by specifying a maximum input level (for the SSA it is –20dBm) and by using an attenuator before the analyser input for larger input levels. The necessary selectivity is obtained by using a superheterodyne receiver design in which image problems are minimised by using an intermediate frequency (IF) which is higher than the maximum frequency of the analyser – in this case 145MHz, which allows a readily available helical filter to be used. Unfortunately the SSA won't cover the 144–146MHz band itself.

Overview

Fig A2.2 shows a block diagram of the SSA. After attenuation, the input signal is fed via a low-pass filter to the first (up-conversion) mixer, where the input frequency

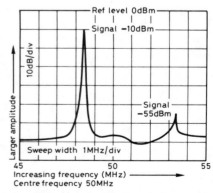

Fig A2.1. A typical screen display of a spectrum analyser

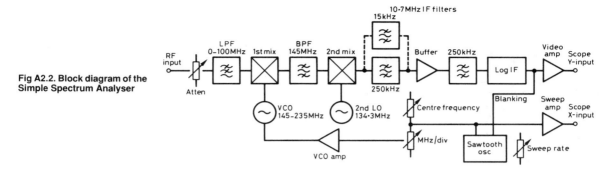

Fig A2.2. Block diagram of the Simple Spectrum Analyser

range of 0–90MHz is mixed with the varicap tuned local oscillator which operates over the range 145–235MHz, giving a first IF of 145MHz. This signal is then passed through the helical filter to a second mixer and local oscillator, where it is down-converted to the second IF of 10.7MHz.

The signal next passes through wide or narrow IF filters, a buffer amplifier and a further wide filter, before entering the logarithmic IF strip. This produces a signal-strength output which is proportional to the log of the strip input, hence the display can be calibrated in dBm. This output (usually termed the 'video output') is then fed to the Y channel of the oscilloscope.

The rest of the SSA is simple. The sweep generator produces a linear ramp sweep voltage, part of which (selected by the sweep width control) is added to a DC

voltage from the centre frequency control. Since varicap oscillators do not have a completely linear voltage/frequency relationship, this sweep voltage is passed to the break-point generator, which puts a 'kink' in the sweep where it will attempt to linearise the frequency sweep over the 70–90MHz portion of the range. The output from the sweep oscillator also drives the X axis input of the oscilloscope.

Not shown on the block diagram is the frequency marker generator, a simple 10MHz crystal oscillator and TTL divider which gives a low-amplitude output, rich in harmonics and which is also fed to the analyser input.

Circuit detail

The SSA is divided into three separate boards. The first and most important is the RF unit (Fig A2.3) which is

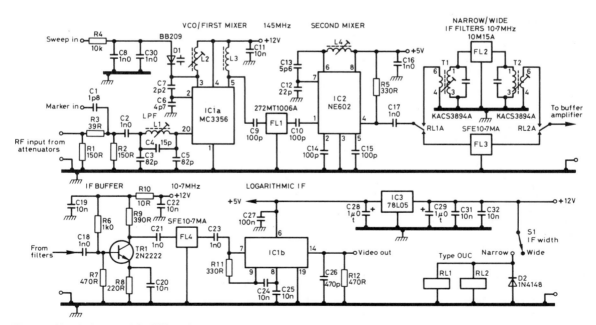

Fig A2.3. Circuit diagram of the RF board

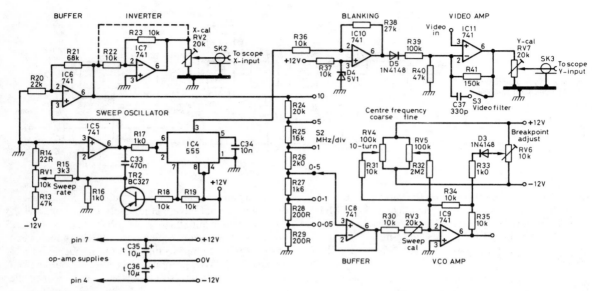

Fig A2.4. Video/sweep circuit

based fairly closely on the original design [1]. The input signal is routed from the front panel 50Ω BNC socket via the two front-panel switched attenuators (shown in Fig A2.5) to a fixed attenuator (R1, 2, 3), which is designed to limit the maximum input to the analyser to about −20dBm and provide something like a consistent 50Ω input. The signal then passes through an elliptical low-pass filter (C3, 4, 5 and L1) to the first mixer, contained in part of IC1, an MC3356. This remarkable device is one of a family of FM receiver chips such as the MC3357 and MC3359 which contain a local oscillator, mixer, limiting IF amplifier and discriminator – better known from NBFM receiver applications.

The MC3356 is intended to be used as a single-chip FSK receiver and has some special features which are exploited in the SSA. First, the IF amplifier has a signal strength output which is proportional to the logarithm of the input voltage and, second, the local oscillator and mixer will work up to at least 250MHz. The local oscillator is varicap tuned by D1 using the sweep voltage from the sweep/video board. Note that two 1n capacitors (C8 and C30) are fitted at the anode end of D1, as a low-impedance path is vital here to enable the highest frequency to be reached. Adding C30 to one of the proto-types increased the upper frequency limit by 5MHz!

The 145MHz IF output from IC1a goes to the first IF filter FL1, a TOKO 3-chamber helical type. The IF output from the filter is then down-converted to the second IF of 10.7MHz in IC2, a NE602 oscillator/mixer chip, the LO frequency of about 134.3MHz being set by L4, C12 and C13. Note that there are some differences between the circuit and values shown here and those in references [1]

and [6]. The values shown in Fig A2.3 are correct and the connection of pin 6 to Vcc, together with the capacitor values, is taken from the manufacturer's data sheet.

Setting the second LO below the first IF removes the 21.4MHz (2 × 2nd IF) spurious response of the original design. The NE602 requires a lower voltage supply than the MC3356 and this is obtained from a 5V regulator, IC3. Narrow (15kHz) or wide (250kHz) first IF filters (FL2 and 3) are selected by means of the miniature relays RL1 and RL2, and the front panel switch S1 (IF BAND-WIDTH).

After filtering, the signal is amplified by TR1, which is run at a relatively high standing current so as to provide good dynamic range. Although the stage does not provide the correct terminations for the filters, in practice this is of little consequence. Removing C20 would improve the matching, but with the consequent loss of over 20dB of sensitivity! The signal is then passed via a second filter (FL4) to the main IF signal processing circuit IC1b. This does one of the most difficult jobs in the analyser: it provides a DC output which is proportional to the log of the IF input voltage. Here in one fell swoop the 10dB/division Y-axis calibration is achieved, with the (video) output being taken via a screened lead to the sweep/video board. The output from the FM discriminator is not used in this application.

Sweep generator

The sweep generator circuit, shown in Fig A2.4, is broadly based on Helfrick's *QST* article [2] with a few changes for use with this particular VCO. In this circuit

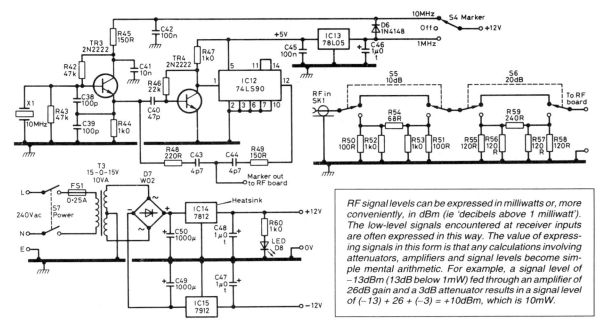

RF signal levels can be expressed in milliwatts or, more conveniently, in dBm (ie 'decibels above 1 milliwatt'). The low-level signals encountered at receiver inputs are often expressed in this way. The value of expressing signals in this form is that any calculations involving attenuators, amplifiers and signal levels become simple mental arithmetic. For example, a signal level of −13dBm (13dB below 1mW) fed through an amplifier of 26dB gain and a 3dB attenuator results in a signal level of (−13) + 26 + (−3) = +10dBm, which is 10mW.

Fig A2.5. Marker generator, PSU and front panel attenuators

741 op-amps have been used throughout as (a) there is no need for anything more sophisticated and (b) they are so cheap that one can be liberal with them!

The sweep ramp is generated by the 555 timer IC4, op-amp IC5 and current source TR2 with the sweep rate being controlled by a front-panel potentiometer, RV1. The 555 also provides a fast blanking-pulse output for the video amplifier. The sweep output is buffered by IC6, before being fed to the sweep width front panel switch S2 (MHz/DIV) and to the X output SK2. Depending on the particular oscilloscope, the inverting unity-gain buffer IC7 may not be needed – if a positive voltage applied to the oscilloscope X input deflects the spot to the right, then IC7 can be omitted. In this instance R22 and R23 are omitted and pin 6 of IC6 is connected to the top of the X CAL preset RV2, via link LK1 as shown by the dotted line.

The selected sweep voltage amplitude from the wiper of S2 is buffered by voltage follower IC8 before amplification in IC9. In this final stage three important things happen: (i) the sweep voltage gain is set to allow a calibrated frequency sweep; (ii) an adjustable DC offset (the centre frequency) is added by means of a 10-turn potentiometer RV4 (CENTRE FREQUENCY COARSE) and RV5 (CENTRE FREQUENCY FINE); and (iii) an adjustable non-linearity (break-point) is deliberately introduced into the linear sweep ramp by means of RV6, D3 and R33. This improves the frequency sweep linearity above 70MHz.

Video amplifier

The video amplifier (IC11) provides a small amount of gain and in conjunction with comparator IC10 provides the retrace blanking by shifting the retrace portion vertically downwards off the screen. Capacitor C37 across the feedback resistor can be switched by S3 (VIDEO FILTER) to provide a little smoothing of the 'grass' on the display if wanted and pre-set RV7 (Y CAL) allows the output of the amplifier to be set to the required 100mV per 10dB of RF input.

The third board, which contains the marker generator and power supply (Fig A2.5), needs little comment. The marker generator uses conventional techniques to produce a comb of 10 and/or 1MHz markers which can be added to the input signal to allow an easy method of frequency calibration. The power supply uses standard components.

Construction

The RF board is constructed on a double-sided glass-epoxy printed circuit board, one side of which is not etched and is used as an earth plane. The component placement diagram (together with drilling details) is shown in Fig A2.6. Most (but not all) of the holes require the copper on the earth plane side to be cleared away around the hole with a counterbore or small drill. Note that the lugs of the shielding cans for FL1 and T1/T2 are used to provide earth paths for tracks underneath the

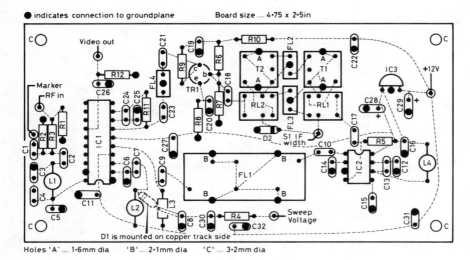

● indicates connection to groundplane   Board size ..... 4·75 x 2·5in

Holes 'A' .... 1·6mm dia   'B' .... 2·1mm dia   'C' .... 3·2mm dia

Fig A2.6. RF board layout (component side). Note that the BB209 D1 is mounted on the underside of the board

board, and so need to be soldered on both sides of the PCB. The small additional holes on the track layout provide locating holes for the earth plane connections of components – small ceramic capacitors these days seem very prone to disintegrating if one of their legs is bent through a right angle! Note that the varicap diode D1 must be mounted on the underside of the board with its cathode close to the end of L2, as shown.

The video/sweep board component placement is shown in Fig A2.8. This is a single-sided PCB where the optional link LK1 (shown dotted) should be fitted instead of R22, R23 and IC7 if you don't need the X output inverter stage, as described earlier. If you do need these components, then omit LK1. Note that the resistors R24–29 are mounted on the rotary switch S2.

The third board, containing the marker generator and the power supply, is also a single-sided PCB. The component overlay is shown in Fig A2.9. Sufficient space for a small heatsink for IC14 has been provided on the board.

The analyser needs to be constructed in a metal case to provide the necessary shielding from stray signals but, when choosing or making a case and installing the boards, remember that the presets on both the RF and sweep boards will need adjustment. This means that the boards should be mounted so that there is easy access to both of them. The input attenuators are constructed on the slide switches S5 and S6 using short leads, and could well be fitted with a grounded screening box made of double-sided PCB.

For the coarse centre-frequency control,

choose a good 10-turn potentiometer and fit it with a large knob which has a cranked handle; this will save a lot of wear and tear on your fingers! The fine control needs a

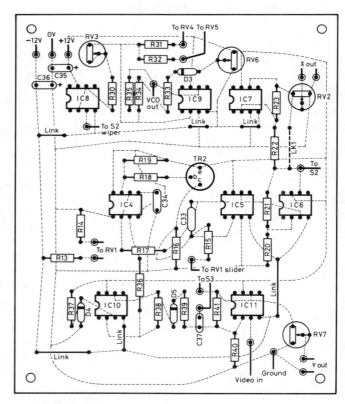

Fig A2.8. Video/sweep board layout (component side)

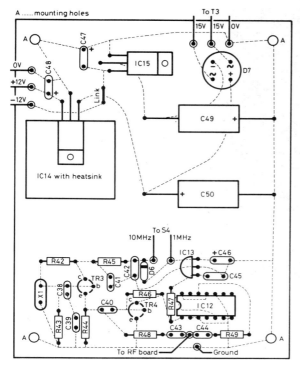

Fig A2.9. Marker generator and PSU layout (component side)

good-quality, single-turn, carbon-track potentiometer. The connections to the RF board from the front-panel attenuators and the marker generator should be with miniature coaxial cable such as RG174. The video and sweep connections, as well as those to S2 and the X and Y output sockets, should be made with small-diameter screened (audio) cable.

Test the boards on the bench before finally assembling them in the case. One of the prototypes spent its first few weeks in this state simply because I could always find something to look at with it which seemed more interesting than the prospect of drilling holes in the front panel! Final setting up of the RF board should be done when it is fixed in the case.

Alignment

Start by testing the power supply and marker generator. The latter can be easily checked by listening to its harmonics on an HF receiver, or by using an oscilloscope on the output of the decade divider. Next test the sweep and video board. It should be fairly easy to check the operation of this with the oscilloscope which will be used for the display. Don't set it up at this stage, merely confirm that the sawtooth waveform is available at the analyser X output, and that an attenuated version (with a

DC offset dependent on the centre frequency controls) is available at the VCO sweep voltage output.

When the RF board is complete, connect power to it and ground the tuning input. Then connect the video output to the oscilloscope (which for the moment can have its conventional timebase operating) and select wide IF bandwidth. If a 145MHz source (eg a 2m handheld with a dummy load) is brought close to the input side of the 145MHz filter, the trace should deflect upwards, showing that the second mixer, oscillator and log IF strip are working. Adjust L4 for maximum response, reducing the input signal as required.

Now complete all the interconnections, set the oscilloscope to external X operation, and connect the X output of the SSA to the external X input of the oscilloscope. Adjust RV2 (X CAL) (and perhaps also the oscilloscope X gain) so that the available sweep is just wider than the screen. Set S2 to 10MHz/DIV, connect the video output of the SSA to the oscilloscope Y input (set to 100mV/cm, DC coupling) and switch on the 10MHz markers. At this stage, a few blips on the screen should be seen. When the VCO is correctly aligned, one of the blips will not disappear when the markers are switched off – this is the lower limit of the coverage – in other words 0MHz.

The next stage requires patience! Set RV4 (CENTRE FREQUENCY COARSE) to about mid travel and unscrew the core of L2 so that it is about half-way out of the coil – by now a few marker blips should be seen if all is well. Adjust L4 for maximum amplitude of the blips, noting that there will be two positions where this occurs – choose the position where the core is further inside the coil, as the other corresponds to the LO being on the high side of the first IF. By careful adjustment of the VCO coil L2 it should be possible to see marker blips every 10MHz up to 90MHz, whilst still keeping the 0MHz blip. If necessary adjust L4 slightly. L1 does not need adjustment – just leave the core as supplied.

Adjust RV3 (SWEEP CAL) and RV6 (SET BREAK-POINT) to give a linear display (as near as possible) over the bottom 70 or 80MHz or so, with one marker appearing at every horizontal division on the screen. You will find that careful setting of RV6 will substantially improve the frequency linearity above 70MHz. These adjustments interact somewhat, so it is worth repeating them. Check, with the aid of the 1MHz markers, the operation of the MHz/DIV (SWEEP WIDTH) switch.

Final adjustment

Now is a good time to finally adjust the filters on the RF board. Using an internal marker blip, carefully adjust the 145MHz filter for maximum signal amplitude. Select the narrow IF, and adjust the cores of T1 and T2 for maximum amplitude and best shape – what is displayed is the actual IF response of the analyser. When using the narrow IF,

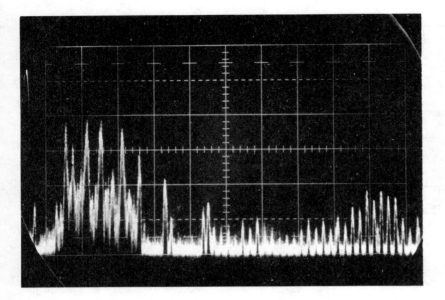

Fig A2.10. Typical SSA display with short antenna. Sweep width is 5MHz/div. The frequency range shown is 5 to 55MHz with 30MHz at the centre of the screen. HF broadcast stations dominate the left portion on the display. Just left of centre are two CB transmissions. Clock frequency harmonics from a microprocessor operating a few feet away can be seen from 30 to 55MHz

remember to reduce the sweep rate. If a marker is put at the centre of the screen with the centre frequency controls, reducing the sweep width with S2 should not result in the marker moving – if it does, then try adjusting the oscilloscope X shift slightly and re-centring the marker.

Finally, the calibration of the log vertical scale must be set using a 50Ω signal source, such as a signal generator connected to the SSA RF input socket. Using the oscilloscope Y shift, position the base line near the bottom of the screen. With the attenuators switched out, and the oscilloscope Y amplifier set to 100mV/cm, adjust the signal amplitude to give a peak of four divisions or so. Now adjust the Y cal preset so that when attenuation is switched in, the peak falls in amplitude by 1cm per 10dB. If you have access to an accurate signal source, you can set the oscilloscope Y shift so that the top of the screen corresponds to −20dBm (in a commercial instrument this is termed the 'reference level'). The noise floor of the analyser is about −85dBm but note that the lowest vertical division doesn't quite correspond to the 10dB per division calibration of the rest of the screen.

Practical hints

Bear in mind the limitations of the analyser – remember that it has a maximum input of −20dBm (+10dBm with both attenuators in), and will start to show its own shortcomings if you overload it – the dynamic range of the analyser is over 50dB. Whilst the absolute sensitivity will vary across its range by 6dB or so, the relative calibration of 10dB per vertical division remains unchanged for any given frequency. When using the narrow IF, slow the sweep down – watching the display whilst you do will soon show you why this is necessary. Incidentally, although not shown on the circuit diagram, one addition I recommend is a good RF filter on the mains input, to keep the entry of RF to the approved route only: via the front-panel input socket!

Whilst you won't find the SSA suitable for making intermodulation distortion measurements or looking at oscillator noise, many useful and interesting tasks await it. By connecting a few feet of wire to the input, a fascinating picture of the HF spectrum emerges – try it during the day and then have another look at night when the 7MHz broadcast stations are in full swing. Use the 10 and 1MHz markers to find your way about the spectrum. You should find that the upper limit of the analyser is over 95MHz, and that if you live in a good signal strength area, Band II VHF radio signals are visible. Connecting a good antenna should enable a watch to be kept for 28 or 50MHz openings. If your HF rig has a mixer VFO, try looking at the output – and be prepared for a shock such as I had when I looked at mine! A photograph of a typical display using a very short antenna can be seen in Fig A2.10.

Whilst it doesn't quite have the performance of a commercial unit (or for that matter the same price tag!), when used with a modicum of care it is a very useful tool. I hope you'll find that, once you have built it, the SSA rapidly becomes indispensable for all kinds of jobs around the shack.

Acknowledgements

First, thanks should go to Al Helfrick, K2BLA, whose inspirational design started this all. Second to the many people who expressed interest in my original design

Table A2.1. Components list

RF BOARD

RESISTORS

R1, 2	150
R3	39
R4	10k
R5, 11	330
R6	1k0
R7, 12	470
R8	220
R9	390
R10	10

CAPACITORS

C1	1p8
C2, 8, 16, 17, 18, 21, 23, 30	1n0
C3, 5	82p
C4	15p
C6	4p7
C7	2p2
C9, 10, 14, 15	100p
C11, 19, 20, 22, 24, 25, 31, 32	10n
C12	22p
C13	5p6
C26	470p
C27	100n
C28, 29	1µ 35V tant bead

SEMICONDUCTORS

D1	BB209
D2	1N4148
TR1	2N2222
IC1	MC3356
IC2	NE602
IC3	78L05

MISCELLANEOUS

FL1	272MT1006A CBT 145MHz helical filter
FL2	10M15A 2 pole 10.7MHz crystal
FL3, 4	SFE10.7MA 10.7MHz ceramic filter
L1, 2	TOKO S18 coil 1.5t white 301SN0100
L3	4.7µH RFC TOKO FL4 348LS4R7
L4	TOKO S18 coil 4.5t yellow 301SN0400
T1, 2	TOKO KACS3894A IFT
RL1, 2	Minature relay type OUC

S1	SPDT min toggle IF BANDWIDTH

MARKER GENERATOR

RESISTORS

R42, 43	47k
R44, 47	1k0
R45, 49	150
R46	22k
R48	220

CAPACITORS

C33, 39	100p
C40	47p
C41	10n
C42, 45	100n
C43, 44	4p7
C46	1µ 35V tant bead

SEMICONDUCTORS

TR3, 4	2N2222
D6	1N4148
IC12	74LS90
IC13	78L05

MISCELLANEOUS

X1	10MHz HC18U
S4	SPDT centre off toggle MARKER

SWEEP AND VIDEO BOARD

RESISTORS

RV1	10k lin SWEEP RATE
RV2	20k cermet preset X CAL
RV3	20k cermet preset SWEEP CAL
RV4	100k 10-turn COARSE CENTRE FREQ
RV5	100k lin carbon FINE CENTRE FREQ
RV6	10k cermet preset BREAKPOINT ADJ
RV7	20k cermet preset Y CAL

(RV2 and RV7 can be any value in the range 10–100k; similarly RV4 and RV5 can be 10–200k).

CAPACITORS

C33	470n polyester layer

C34	10n
C35, 36	10µ 25V tant bead
C37	330p

SEMICONDUCTORS

TR2	BC327
D3, 4	1N4148
D5	5V1 zener
IC4	555
IC5–11	741

MISCELLANEOUS

S2	1 pole 6 way wafer MHz/ DIV
S3	SPST or SPDT toggle VIDEO FILTER
SK2, 3	BNC panel socket

POWER SUPPLY

RESISTOR

R60	1k0

CAPACITORS

C47, 48	1µ 35V tant bead
C49, 50	1000µ 25 or 35V elec

SEMICONDUCTORS

D7	W02 bridge rectifier
D8	red panel-mounting LED
IC14	7812 with small heatsink
IC15	7912

MISCELLANEOUS

T3	15-0-15V 10VA mains transformer
S7	DPST ON OFF
F1	0.25A fuse and holder

FRONT-PANEL ATTENUATORS

R50, 51	100
R52, 53	1k0
R54	68
R55–58	120
R59	240
S5, 6	DPDT slide switch 10dB (S5), 20dB (S6)
SK1	BNC panel-mount socket

All resistors are 0.25W 5% or better; capacitors are miniature ceramic plate type unless otherwise noted.

mentioned in *TT* (I'm sorry I couldn't reply to you all); to G3SEK for reading the draft, and finally to G8HAJ who provided material assistance with the early development.

References

[1] 'A simple spectrum analyzer', A Helfrick, *RF Design* January 1988, pp35–37. Details also given in 'Technical Topics', *Radio Communication* April 1988.

[2] 'An inexpensive spectrum analyzer for the radio amateur', A Helfrick, K2BLA, *QST* November 1985, pp23–29.

[3] 'Technical Topics', *Radio Communication* July 1988.

[4] 'Technical Topics', *Radio Communication* August 1988. These notes are very definitely no longer available!

[5] 'Technical Topics', *Radio Communication* September 1988.

[6] 'Technical Topics', *Radio Communication* November 1988.

PCBs and components

Photocopies of the PCB track details are available from the *Radio Communication* office at RSGB Headquarters. Please send a stamped, self-addressed envelope of foolscap size and clearly mark your envelope 'Spectrum Analyser'.

At the time of going to press of this book (1992), component kits and PCBs for this project were being advertised in *Radio Communication*.

Update

The above article is reproduced as it appeared in Radio Communication. *The author, Roger Blackwell, G4PMK, has kindly advised the following amendments and corrections which should be noted.*

1. R21 on the sweep board circuit diagram should be 6k8, not 68k.

2. The list of fixed resistors was omitted from the sweep board components list:

R13, 40	47k
R14	22R
R15	3k3
R16, 17, 33	1k0
R18, 19, 22, 23, 30, 31, 34–37	10k
R20	22k
R21	6k8
R24	20k
R25	16k
R26	2k0

R27	1k6
R28, 29	200R
R32	2M2
R38	27k
R39	100k
R41	150k

3. The diodes were incorrectly shown in the sweep board component list. They should read as follows:

D3, 5	1N4148
D4	5V1 zener

4. In the RF board components list the entry for D1 should read as follows:

D1	BB209 (MV209, BB809 possible substitutes)

5. On the RF board a 1n0 capacitor should be inserted between pin 6 of the NE602 and the junction of L4 and C13. (This is a change because Phillips later advised the author that pin 6 should *not* have a DC path to Vcc.)

6. In Fig 9 there should be a dotted line (indicating track) between C38/C39 junction and the emitter of TR3.

7. The effective bypassing of the varicap diode D1 is important if maximum frequency span is to be obtained. This may be achieved by the addition of two leadless disc or trapezoidal capacitors fitted in slots cut in the board. One should be fitted next to the track by the varicap. The track should be cut between this new capacitor and the existing two 1n0 capacitors, and the cut bridged with a 47k resistor. The second capacitor should be fitted as close to pin 4 of IC1 as possible. The other sides of both capacitors are soldered to the ground plane.

8. Note that IC sockets must *not* be used on the RF board.

Characteristics of various filters and ferrites for amateur radio EMC use

This appendix is a report on work carried out by Dave Lauder, G1OSC, at the request of the RSGB's EMC Committee. The performance of the filters and chokes has been measured under defined conditions, and comments made on their effectiveness. The author is professionally involved in EMC, mainly in the field of education and training.

The filters and chokes described are for use with broadcast radios, TVs or other affected equipment. They are not suitable for use at the output of an amateur transmitter.

Table A3.1 summarises the characteristics of various filters and ferrites for EMC use on various amateur bands. For an explanation of common-mode (in-phase) and differential-mode (anti-phase) signals, see Chapter 5 and also later in this appendix. Common-mode signals can be caused by amateur transmissions on any band where the braid of a TV antenna coaxial cable, rather than the antenna itself, acts as a receiving antenna for amateur signals, particularly at HF where a UHF TV antenna itself is not an efficient receiving antenna.

In the 'stop-band loss' column, the bar graphs represent the minimum filter loss in a particular amateur band to the nearest 5dB. The higher the stop-band loss, the better. One square represents 10dB which may cure minor breakthrough, but in most cases 20dB, 30dB or more may be required. Six squares represent 60dB or more.

In the 'pass-band loss' column, the bar graphs represent the loss in the UHF TV band to the nearest 1dB. The lower the pass-band loss, the better. In the case of the HPF2, the pass band includes the FM radio broadcast band (Band 2, 87.5 to 108MHz) as well as the UHF TV band. Many of the filters have 'N/A' in the FM broadcast pass-band loss column which means 'not applicable', ie the filter is not suitable for passing this band.

Where the UHF TV signal strength is high, a loss of 3 to 5dB may not be noticeable but, if the signal is weak, then even a 2dB loss could give a slight but noticeable increase in noise on the picture.

In some cases, the pass-band loss of a filter varies in different parts of the UHF TV band, particularly on the lowest channels. In this case, the relevant curve on Figs A3.10 to A3.14 should be examined to find the loss for the UHF TV channels used in a particular area. (See Appendix 5 for vision carrier frequencies of UHF TV channels).

For ease of reference, all figures and the table are grouped at the end of this appendix.

Filters

For each filter, the principal characteristics are described, together with equivalent circuits and measured response curves for a typical filter. The responses are subject to some variation between samples of the same type, particularly in the case of the home-constructed filter. The test methods are described later.

Home-constructed high-pass filter and braid-breaker

Circuit and layout: see Fig A3.19.
Response curves: see Figs A3.1, A3.2, A3.10 (pass band), A3.15 (common mode).
Type: balanced L-C high-pass filter (UHF TV) with braid-breaking.
Pass band: Bands 4 and 5 (UHF TV).
Loss in pass band: typically 0.5–2dB.
Braid-breaking action: capacitive.
Remarks: This filter can be constructed at low cost, making it particularly useful where a number of such filters are required. It has good rejection of HF differential-mode signals but rejection of common-mode signals is not as good as a transformer-type braid-breaker. It is not particularly effective at 144MHz.

Fig A3.1 shows the response of this filter and the AKD HPF1 in a test circuit with a common ground between the input and output. This test bypasses the capacitor in series with the braid and gives sharp resonances which are unlikely to occur in practice at the frequencies shown. Fig A3.2 shows the response of the two filters with a 'floating' source (see 'Test methods' later).

AKD HPF1 high-pass filter

Equivalent circuit: see Fig A3.20.
Response curves: see Figs A3.1, A3.2, A3.10 (pass band), A3.15 (common mode).

Type: L-C high-pass filter (UHF TV) with braid-breaker.
Pass band: Bands 4 and 5 (UHF TV).
Loss in pass band: typically 0.5–2dB.
Braid-breaking action: capacitive.
Remarks: Similar performance to home-constructed filter above but slightly better stop-band performance. See notes in previous section regarding test methods.

AKD HPF2 high-pass filter
Equivalent circuit: see Fig A3.21.
Response curves: see Figs A3.3 (stop band), A3.11 (pass band).
RSGB description: Filter 2, high pass for FM broadcast Band 2.
Type: L-C high-pass filter (FM broadcast).
Pass band: Bands 2 (FM radio broadcast), up to 4 and 5 (UHF TV)
Loss in pass band: typically less than 1dB in most of Band 2 (2.5dB at 87.5MHz), 1–3dB in Bands 4 and 5.
Braid-breaking action: none.
Remarks: It is intended for reducing breakthrough on FM broadcast receivers (87.5–108MHz), particularly from HF signals but is also useful for rejecting 50MHz signals. It is only effective against differential-mode signals as it has no braid-breaking action, but an HPF2 with a BB1 or ferrite common-mode choke can be used together if this is required.

AKD HPF6 high-pass filter
Equivalent circuit and appearance: see Fig A3.22.
Response curves: see Figs A3.4 (differential mode overall), A3.12 (pass band).
RSGB description: Filter 8, six-section for UHF TV.
Type: equivalent to six-section L-C high-pass filter (UHF TV), sharp cut-off.
Pass band: Bands 4, 5 (UHF TV).
Loss in pass band: typically 1–3dB (Channels 21–40), 1–2dB (Channels 41–68).
Braid-breaking action: None.
Remarks: The HPF6 is a high-performance filter with a very sharp cut-off below 470MHz. This is the most effective filter for reducing breakthrough from the 430–440MHz amateur band. If a UHF TV masthead preamplifier is in use, the HPF6 should be mounted in a weatherproof box between the antenna and the preamplifier.

Trace B on Fig A3.4 shows the measured response of an HPF6 with 40dB loss at 435MHz. If the coaxial plug on the flying lead was grounded to the metal case of the filter, the response improved as shown in trace C with 50dB loss measured at 435MHz.

Mutek XBF700 television band stripline filter
Appearance: see Fig A3.23.
Response curves: see Figs A3.5 (differential mode overall) and A3.12 (pass band).

Type: stripline band-pass filter (UHF TV).
Pass band: Bands 4, 5 (UHF TV).
Loss in pass band: typically 2–3dB, channels 24–65, rising to 9dB on channel 21, and 4dB on channel 68.
Braid-breaking action: none.
Remarks: This is the only filter tested with a stop band which includes 1.3 GHz. It is also useful at 430–440MHz and good on the 144MHz band and below. The pass-band loss rises at the top of Band 5 and at the lower end of Band 4, particularly on channels 21 and 22. The XBF700 is a stripline filter PCB (size 145×57mm) which requires the addition of connectors or flying leads and a case.

The loss measured above 1GHz is affected by stray capacitive coupling between the input and output of the filter. The result shown in Fig A3.5 is likely to be representative of the performance of the filter in practice, although better performance may be measured using an improved test set-up.

AKD BB1 braid-breaker
Equivalent circuit: see Fig A3.24.
Response curves: see Figs A3.6 (differential mode overall), A3.13 (pass band), A3.15 (common mode).
RSGB description: Filter 1, braid-breaker.
Type: 1:1 transformer braid-breaker.
Pass band: below 10MHz to over 1GHz.
Loss in pass band: typically 2dB over most of its range but 3 to 4dB at UHF channels 50–68.
Braid-breaking action: 1:1 transformer.
Remarks: The BB1 is a transformer-type braid-breaker which is more effective against common-mode signals picked up 'on the braid' than a capacitive braid-breaker such as the HPF1. The BB1 is particularly effective at HF. The braid-breaking action diminishes at VHF due to interwinding capacitance of the transformer, with only 7–8dB loss to common-mode signals in the 144MHz band. A BB1 can be cascaded with other filters such as HPF2, HPF6 or XBF700 which do not have any braid-breaking action, although the total pass-band loss is then the sum of the pass-band losses (in decibels) of the two filters.

Although not intended as a high-pass filter, the differential mode response of a BB1 starts to roll off below 10MHz, with some attenuation to differential mode signals in the 3.5 and 1.8MHz bands.

A BB1 can also be effective on the 1.8, 3.5 and 7MHz bands in reducing HF interference produced by TV line timebase harmonics by preventing them from being radiated by the braid of the TV antenna cable.

Where a braid-breaker is required with negligible insertion loss to differential-mode signals at all frequencies, a common-mode choke may be used (see 'Ferrites' sections below). A suitable type of common-mode choke can be a more effective braid-breaker than a BB1 at VHF, but the BB1 will generally be more effective at HF.

AKD HPFS high-pass filter (special)

Equivalent circuit: see Fig A3.25.
Response curves: see Figs A3.6 (differential mode overall), A3.13 (pass band), A3.15 (common mode).
RSGB description: Filter 3, high-pass for UHF TV.
Type: L-C high-pass filter with transformer braid-breaker.
Pass band: Bands 4, 5 (UHF TV).
Loss in pass band: typically 3–4dB (Channels 21–40), 4–5dB (Channels 41–68).
Braid-breaking action: 1:1 transformer.
Remarks: The HPFS is similar to a BB1 and HPF1 combined. See BB1 section above for braid-breaking performance. It has very effective rejection of differential-mode signals on the 144MHz band and below. Due to the relatively high pass-band loss, this filter is not suitable for areas where the TV signal strength is low.

AKD RBF1/70cm notch filter

Equivalent circuit: see Fig A3.26.
Response curves: see Figs A3.7 (differential mode overall), A3.14 (pass band).
Type: series-resonant trap between inner conductor and braid.
RSGB description: Filter 5, notch tuned to 435MHz.
Pass band: Bands 4, 5 (UHF TV).
Loss in pass band: typically 2–5dB (Channels 21–30), 1–2dB (Channels 31–68).
Braid-breaking action: none.
Remarks: The RBF1 is called a 'radar blip filter' because it was designed to notch out airport radar signals on UHF TV channel 36. The RBF1/70cm version is pre-tuned to 435MHz, although it is possible to adjust the tuning if necessary by means of a trimmer capacitor which is accessible through a hole in the plastic sleeving under the label. A non-metallic trim tool should be used to avoid detuning, as neither side of the trimmer capacitor is grounded. The RBF1 also has a high-pass action with useful rejection of HF differential-mode signals.

AKD TNF2 tuned notch filter range (VHF)

Equivalent circuit: see Fig A3.27.
Response curves: see Figs A3.8 (stop band), A3.14 (pass band), A3.16 (common mode).

AKD type	RSGB description
TNF2/2 metres	Filter 4, notch tuned to 145MHz
TNF2/70MHz	Filter 7, notch tuned to 70MHz
TNF2/50MHz	Filter 6, notch tuned to 50MHz

Type: L-C notch filters in series with inner conductor and braid.
Pass band: Bands 4, 5 (UHF TV).
Loss in pass band: typically 0.5–2dB (Channels 21–40), 2dB (Channels 41–68)
Braid-breaking action: Resonant, only at tuned frequency.

Remarks: Each filter provides rejection of differential-mode and common signals over a certain range of frequencies only. All have low insertion loss in UHF TV Bands 4 and 5. None of the VHF notch filters is suitable for passing FM broadcast Band 2 signals due to the high insertion loss in Band 2.

The test methods used to obtain Figs A3.8 and A3.16 are different from the test methods used by the manufacturer of the filters. This may be why some of the notches measured do not coincide exactly with the specified amateur bands. Nevertheless, in most cases there is still a good level of attenuation in the specified band. See later for details of test methods.

Where a UHF TV pre-amplifier or a distribution amplifier is used, a filter will generally be required on the input side of the amplifier. The TNF2 type of tuned notch filter is not recommended in such cases as it may increase rather than decrease the unwanted signal or may cause the amplifier to oscillate.

AKD TNF2 tuned notch filter range (HF)

Equivalent circuit: see Fig A3.27.
Response curves: see Figs A3.9 (stop band), A3.14 (pass band), A3.17 (common mode).

AKD type	RSGB description
TNF2/10	Filter 10, notch tuned to 28MHz
TNF2/15	Filter 15, notch tuned to 21MHz
TNF2/20	Filter 20, notch tuned to 14MHz

Type: L-C notch filters in series with inner conductor and braid.
Pass band: Bands 4, 5 (UHF TV).
Loss in pass band: typically 0.5–2dB (Channels 21–40), 2dB (Channels 41–68).
Braid-breaking action: resonant, only at tuned frequency.
Remarks: Each filter provides rejection of differential-mode and common-mode signals over a certain range of frequencies only. All have low insertion loss on UHF TV Bands 4 and 5. Most are not suitable for passing FM broadcast Band 2 signals except TNF2/20. For amateur bands below 14MHz, tuned notch filters are not generally used as a high-pass filter/braid-breaker will normally be equally effective.

The test methods used to obtain Figs A3.9 and A3.17 are different from the test methods used by the manufacturer of the filters. This may be why some of the notches measured do not coincide exactly with the specified amateur bands. Nevertheless, in most cases there is still a good level of attenuation in the specified band. See later for details of test methods.

Where a UHF TV preamplifier or a distribution amplifier is used, a filter will generally be required on the input side of the amplifier. The TNF2 type of tuned notch filter is not recommended in such cases as it may increase rather than decrease the unwanted signal; or may cause the amplifier to oscillate; or may result in breakthrough from HF broadcast transmissions.

Home-constructed 145MHz tuned braid-breaker

Equivalent circuit: see Fig A3.28(a).
Response curves: see Fig A3.18 (common mode).
Type: 145MHz tuned common-mode choke ('braid-breaker').
Pass band: DC to Bands 4, 5 (UHF TV) and above.
Loss to differential-mode signals: negligible.
Braid-breaking action: resonant, only in 144–146MHz band.
Remarks: This filter can be used to provide a useful amount of 'braid-breaking' action on the 144–146MHz band. It has negligible effect on differential-mode signals but can be cascaded with another filter.

Fig A3.28(b) shows the method of construction. The outer sleeving should be removed from a length of 75Ω coaxial cable in two places 75mm apart. At each point, a piece of bare wire should be wrapped around the braid and soldered all round, taking care to avoid melting the insulation inside the braid. A small piece of circuit board with the copper removed should be used to provide mechanical support.

This filter must be tuned carefully before installation, using a non-metallic trim tool. A dip oscillator can be used to find the resonant frequency of the loop of cable or, if one is not available, the arrangement shown in Fig A3.28(c) can be used. The trimmer capacitor should be adjusted carefully to give minimum signal on the receiver's S-meter.

Tuned braid-breakers of this type can be made for use on a particular amateur band at 70MHz or below by using more turns of coaxial cable. Thin 75Ω coaxial cable such as RG179B/U or miniature RG59 will be required. At HF a ferrite core is recommended, either a rod or a ring core. The loss of the ferrite should not be too high at the resonant frequency, otherwise the resonance will be severely damped. If a dip meter is used to find the resonant frequency of a ring core, a coupling winding will be required because the ring core forms a closed magnetic path.

Ferrites

Various types of ferrite cores can be used to make common-mode chokes on coaxial cables, mains cables and audio cables etc. These chokes introduce a series impedance to unwanted common-mode signals picked up from a transmitter but have negligible effect on the wanted differential-mode signal in the cable.

In each test, the maximum number of turns used is the maximum possible number of turns of 6mm diameter cable which can be wound on the core or cores. The only exception to this is AKD Unifilters where 4mm diameter cable was used for the eight-turn windings. With some cores at VHF, performance is improved by winding fewer than the maximum number of turns. This is due to stray capacitance in parallel with the winding, which should in any case be minimised by using the winding method shown in Fig A4.3 (Appendix 4). Some types of ferrite are good insulators but others are sufficiently conductive to increase the capacitive coupling between the two ends of a winding.

Pair of Neosid 28-041-28 Ferrite ring cores (RSGB type)

Fig A3.35 shows the dimensions of these cores. Fig A3.29, trace B, shows the performance between 0–30MHz of a 14-turn winding on a pair of Neosid 28-041-28 ferrite rings of the type supplied by RSGB. Fig A3.32, trace B, shows the same winding between 0–200MHz. Trace C on Fig A3.32 shows a seven-turn winding which gives better performance above 60MHz. The seven-turn winding was wound as shown in Fig A4.3 to keep the ends separated. A further reduction to three turns does not improve the VHF performance at any frequency.

If wound with coaxial cable, the resulting common-mode choke can be more effective than a BB1 braid-breaker at 145MHz but with negligible insertion loss to differential-mode signals (such loss is only the loss in the length of coaxial cable wound through the ring and the loss in any additional coaxial connectors.) Semi-airspaced coaxial cable is not suitable for winding with such tight bends as it may collapse internally and short-circuit. For more than about 10 turns it will probably be necessary to use a length of miniature 75Ω coaxial cable such as miniature RG59 or RG179B/U. The loss of a 1m length of such cable at the top of Band 5 is less than 0.5dB for miniature RG59 and less than 0.8dB for RG179B/U.

Philips ferrite ring core 4322-020-97200

This is a Philips Components RCC36/23/15 ring core, made of grade 4C65 ferrite with a violet coating to indicate the grade of ferrite. The dimensions are shown in Fig A3.35. In 1992, these were available through Philips Components trade distributors such as ESD Electronic Services (formerly STC) of Harlow (Stock No 058352E) and Hawnt Electronics Ltd. One of these cores is significantly more expensive than a pair of the Neosid ring cores above but requires fewer turns and gives substantially improved performance at 21MHz and above. Below 14MHz, the use of a pair of Neosid 28-041-28 rings is recommended due to the higher permeability of the ferrite.

Fig A3.29, trace C, shows the 0–30MHz performance of a single Philips 4322-020-97200 ring core wound with eight turns. Fig A3.32, trace D, shows the performance of the same ring at 0–200MHz. Due to the smaller inside diameter, the maximum possible number of turns of 6mm diameter cable is eight.

Clip-on chokes – split-bead type

Where a cable cannot be disconnected or connectors cannot be removed, split ferrite cores which can be clipped around a cable might appear to be an attractive option, but in practice they are only likely to be effective if enough turns can be wound on the core. Large split ferrite beads are available in various sizes for circular cables and two-part ferrite bars are available for fitting to flat ribbon cables.

Clip-on chokes designed for single-turn applications normally fit closely round the cable, forming a tube of ferrite 25mm or more long. The main application of such single-turn chokes is to reduce VHF radiated emissions from equipment by a few decibels in order to meet a particular standard. They can also be effective for damping cable resonances. For a significant reduction in emissions or breakthrough, however, particularly in the lower HF bands, 5–15 turns may be required.

Fig A3.37 shows the appearance and dimensions of a split bead, Archer type 273-105, which is described as a 'snap-together ferrite data-line filter' and was available from Tandy in 1992. Its response was tested by fitting it to a length of cable forming a 'one turn' choke. With any ferrite ring or bead, if the cable passes through the hole in the core once, then this is 'one turn', even if it passes straight through.

Fig A3.33, trace B, shows the response of a 200mm length of 6mm diameter coaxial cable braid from 0–200MHz and trace D shows the response of the same length of braid with the ferrite choke fitted. At 145MHz for example, the additional loss introduced by clipping on the ferrite is the difference between traces B and D, which is 7dB. This is fairly typical of the performance of split beads of this size.

Clip-on choke – 'U' core type – AKD Unifilter

The AKD Unifilter clip-on choke was available in packs of four (UF4) or eight (UF8) from AKD and from Cirkit Distribution Ltd in 1992. Fig A3.38 shows the dimensions of a Unifilter and Fig A3.39 shows a common-mode choke using a Unifilter. Similar items may also be available from other sources.

Fig A3.30 shows the characteristics of a pair of AKD Unifilters (four 'U' half-cores) from 0–30MHz. Trace B shows four turns on two Unifilters and trace C shows eight turns on two Unifilters. In order to fit eight turns in the core window, the maximum cable diameter is 4mm. Trace D shows eight turns on a Philips 4322-020-97200 ring core for comparison.

For effective suppression at 14–70MHz using Unifilters, the number of turns squared multiplied by the number of cores should equal about 200 or more. This could be achieved with 14 turns on a single core (two halves) but, as the area of the core window is substantially less than for

a 25.4mm inside diameter ring, there is unlikely to be room for 14 turns except with thin loudspeaker cable. For thicker cables, more cores will be required to provide the same impedance, for example, 10 turns on two cores (four halves), seven turns on four cores (eight halves) or five turns on eight cores (16 halves). Due to the lower permeability of the ferrite, Unifilters are less effective than Neosid 28-041-28 cores below 14MHz and far less effective at 7MHz and below.

Fig A3.33, trace C, shows the response of a single turn on four Unifilters from 0–200MHz. The difference between a 200mm length of cable with no ferrite and the same length of cable with four Unifilters is the difference between traces B and C which is 3dB at 28MHz and 2dB at 145MHz.

When using any type of split bead or clip-on choke it is important to ensure that the cable or winding does not force the cores apart, as any air gap between the halves of the core greatly reduces the inductance. The two halves of the AKD Unifilter cores are clipped together securely with a releasable cable tie, whereas the clip arrangement of some other types of split 'U' core is less effective and pulling the cable tight can move the core halves apart, leaving a slight gap.

Ferrite rods

An MW/LW ferrite antenna rod can be used to make a common-mode choke as shown in Fig A3.40. Fig A3.31 compares ferrite rods and a Philips 4322-020-97200 ring core from 0–30MHz. Fig A3.34 compares the same cores from 0–200MHz. On both figures, trace B shows 10 turns of 6mm diameter cable close wound on a ferrite rod 125mm long by 9.5mm diameter and trace C shows 25 turns on a 200mm × 9.5mm rod. At 28MHz and above, ferrite rods can be more effective than Neosid 28-041-28 ring cores but are somewhat larger. At 145MHz, the 25-turn winding on a ferrite rod is at least as good as eight turns on a Philips 4322-020-97200 ring core, and is significantly better than seven turns on a pair of Neosid 28-041-28 cores or four turns on two AKD Unifilters.

A ferrite rod should not be wound with semi-airspaced coaxial cable as the tight bend radius may cause the cable to collapse internally and short-circuit. The 25-turn winding requires about 1.2m of cable.

Test methods

A Hewlett-Packard 8591A spectrum analyser with tracking generator was used for the tests. A tracking generator is a signal generator which is built into a spectrum analyser and whose output frequency follows (tracks) the frequency sweep of the spectrum analyser. When the tracking generator output is fed via a filter to the spectrum analyser's RF input, the frequency response of the filter is displayed.

Due to the noise floor of the spectrum analyser and the additional attenuators used, measurements of filter loss greater than 60dB could not be made, hence losses greater than 55dB are not shown on the response curves.

Differential mode, 75Ω

Figs A3.41 and A3.42 show the test set-up for measuring differential-mode characteristics of filters which have transformer braid-breaking or no braid-breaking. The 50Ω output of the tracking generator is connected via a 10dB attenuator with 50Ω input impedance and 75Ω output impedance to the filter under test. Another attenuator with 75Ω input impedance and 50Ω output impedance is used to match the output of the filter under test into the 50Ω input of the spectrum analyser. The resistor values shown are designed to give a true 10dB power loss, for example 0dBm in 50Ω at the tracking generator output results in −10dBm in 75Ω at the output of the attenuator.

Above 600MHz, most of the filters tested allow some UHF signal to pass from the inner of the coaxial cable to the outside of the braid, resulting in standing waves on the outside of the cable. These standing waves cause variations in the apparent filter loss, depending on the exact cable length used. To give more repeatable test results, a ferrite clip-on choke is fitted to the output lead of the filter under test to attenuate such signals on the outside of the coaxial cable.

The arrangement in Fig A3.41 is used to give the 0dB reference trace, then the filter under test is plugged in as shown in Fig A3.42. For the 2dB/division pass-band loss tests, the reference trace is not perfectly flat but has up to ±0.25dB ripple at UHF. For the 2dB/division curves, the filter loss is the difference between the filter response trace and the reference trace.

When the filter is actually in use, however, the source and load impedances which are presented to it may be far from 75Ω, particularly at frequencies far outside the UHF TV bands. This means that its loss in practice may be significantly different from the test results.

Differential mode, 75Ω, floating source

Figs A3.43 and A3.44 show the test set-up for measuring differential-mode characteristics of filters which have an impedance in series with the braid as well as in series with the inner conductor. A BB1 braid-breaker is used to provide a 'floating' source, that is a source with neither side grounded to the chassis of the spectrum analyser. At HF, this is close to a true 'floating' source, but at VHF, and especially above 150MHz, the interwinding capacitance of the BB1 transformer makes the source 'float' less well. A clip-on ferrite choke was fitted to the output lead of the filter under test.

This test method was used when testing the HPF1, all the TNF2 range and the home-constructed high-pass filter/braid-breaker. The 0dB reference traces take account of the additional loss introduced by the BB1 so that the curves show only the loss of the filter under test. The filter responses are not shown below 10MHz because the response of the BB1 transformer starts to fall off.

If the test set-up shown in Fig A3.42 is used for filters with an impedance in series with the braid, the common ground between input and output short-circuits the impedance which is in series with the ground side of the filter, affecting the response of the filter. Fig A3.1 shows the response of two filters using the test method in the previous section but without the ferrite choke. Fig A3.2 shows the response with the 'floating source' test method, which is more likely to be representative of what happens in practice.

In the case of the tuned notch filters (see Fig A3.27), there is some interaction between the two tuned circuits L1/C1 and L2/C2, making it difficult to tune the filter so that it gives a differential-mode notch and a common-mode notch at the same frequency. In some cases the notch is not centred on the specified amateur band but the filter still provides a useful attenuation on the latter.

When the filter is actually in use, the differential-mode current on the inner conductor which flows through L1/C1 returns via the braid and L2/C2, except for a small proportion of the current which returns via stray capacitances external to the filter. The 'floating' source test models this situation with nearly equal but antiphase currents through L1/C1 and L2/C2. The two tuned circuits are in series as far as differential-mode signals are concerned, and this test shows a double notch response for some of the filters. In practice, the actual notch frequencies may also be affected by stray capacitances which are effectively in parallel with the tuned circuit L2/C2.

Common-mode filter test, 50Ω

Fig A3.45 illustrates the situation where unwanted signals are picked up by the outside of a coaxial cable braid acting as a receiving antenna. These unwanted signals appear to come from a source impedance which is not well defined but which could be hundreds of ohms, except in the case where the coaxial cable forms a resonant antenna for a particular amateur band. These unwanted signals flow via the chassis of the TV or other equipment and then to earth via capacitance and via the mains earth wire if any. Where there is no mains earth wire, there is still an RF path to earth via the mains due to capacitance from the chassis of the equipment to the mains 'live' and neutral, and capacitance from these conductors to earth. (In PME installations, the mains neutral and earth are joined where the supply enters the house.) The 'load' impedance seen by common-mode signals is also not well defined but could be hundreds of ohms.

Amateur signals may also cause common-mode signals

directly in the mains cable, either due to pick-up in the mains cable itself or in the mains wiring of the house. In such cases a common-mode choke is required.

In order to reduce the common-mode current resulting from this unwanted pick-up, it is necessary to introduce an impedance in series with the unwanted signal path without significantly affecting the wanted differential-mode signal flowing in the TV antenna cable, the mains cable or other cable. This common-mode impedance should be relatively large compared to the sum of the source and load impedances of the common-mode signal. This means that a filter which shows an attenuation of, for example, 20dB to common-mode signals in a 50Ω test circuit may give significantly less common-mode rejection in practice because the source and load impedances are likely to be greater than 50Ω near the affected equipment.

Unwanted common-mode (in-phase) signals are sometimes loosely referred to as being 'on the braid' of a coaxial cable, meaning that there is an RF voltage between the braid of the cable and earth, but the phrase 'on the braid' obscures the fact that there must also be an equal RF voltage between the inner and earth. The braid and the inner are connected together at the TV antenna by a low-impedance folded-dipole element. Therefore, if there is a signal which is on the outside of the braid with respect to earth but which was not picked up by the TV antenna itself, then an equal or nearly equal signal must also exist on the inner with respect to earth, although it can only be measured at the ends of the cable. In any case, with a perfectly shielded coaxial cable, a signal outside the cable cannot pass through the shield and produce a potential difference between the inner conductor and the inside of the braid. To reduce common-mode currents it is therefore necessary to introduce an impedance in series with both the braid and the inner, either by winding the cable through a ring core or by using a filter which has impedance in series with both the braid and the inner.

Figs A3.46 and A3.47 show the test set-up for common-mode testing of filters which have any form of braid-breaking action. The 50Ω output of the tracking generator is connected to a 10dB attenuator with 50Ω input and output impedance. This attenuator also provides an approximate 50Ω termination for the tracking generator even when the impedance on the output of the attenuator is far from 50Ω, thus minimising standing waves in the input cable to the test jig. A second 10dB attenuator with 50Ω input and output impedances ensures that the filter under test is presented with a load impedance very close to 50Ω.

The input and output of the filter under test are terminated with 75Ω resistors to simulate the actual conditions of use, although in practice the source and load impedances may be significantly different from 75Ω at frequencies below UHF. The fact that the filter is designed to be used in 75Ω circuits is of little relevance to common-mode signals. The common-mode performance has been measured in a 50Ω circuit to be consistent with the test method in the next section.

In the case of the TNF2 range of tuned notch filters (see Fig A3.27), the two tuned circuits L1/C1 and L2/C2 are effectively in parallel as far as common-mode signals are concerned but in series as far as differential-mode signals are concerned.

Common-mode ferrite test, 50Ω

This type of measurement in the field of EMC is normally made with 50Ω source and load impedances. Fig A3.48 shows the test set-up for measuring the characteristics of common-mode chokes wound onto ferrite rings and other types of core. Fig A3.46 shows the configuration for the 0dB reference trace.

This test method is similar to the test method in the previous section except that where a ferrite ring is wound with coaxial cable, it makes no difference to the result whether the signal is driven onto the braid only or onto the braid and inner together.

As mentioned above, the source and load impedances for common-mode signals are not well defined and could be as high as several hundred ohms. Thus a common-mode choke which shows an attenuation of, for example, 20dB in a 50Ω circuit may give significantly less common-mode rejection in practice.

Any common-mode chokes with a measured loss greater than 20dB at VHF tend to be very sensitive to the stray capacitance of nearby conducting objects so that the repeatability of such measurements is poor. The test method used for common-mode tests on chokes and filters was not considered suitable for frequencies above 200MHz.

If a spectrum analyser with tracking generator is not available, the test jig shown in Fig A3.48 can still be used to make measurements at spot frequencies or to adjust the tuning of a tuned common-mode choke. The 10dB 50Ω attenuators can be omitted if only relative measurements are required. The signal source could be a signal generator or a steady signal such as a beacon received by an amateur antenna. The signal level at the output of the test jig can be measured by any receiver tuned to the required frequency, provided it has an S-meter. Ideally the S-meter should have a large scale which has been calibrated in decibels relative to 1μV against a signal generator, or calibrated against a beacon or other source in decibels relative to the weakest signal detectable on the S-meter (S1 reading) using a calibrated variable attenuator. With a calibrated S-meter, the loss of various common-mode chokes can be measured in decibels. With a meter calibrated only in S-points, useful relative measurements can still be made to compare two different chokes at a particular frequency or to tune a tuned braid-breaker.

Table A3.1. Summary of filter performance

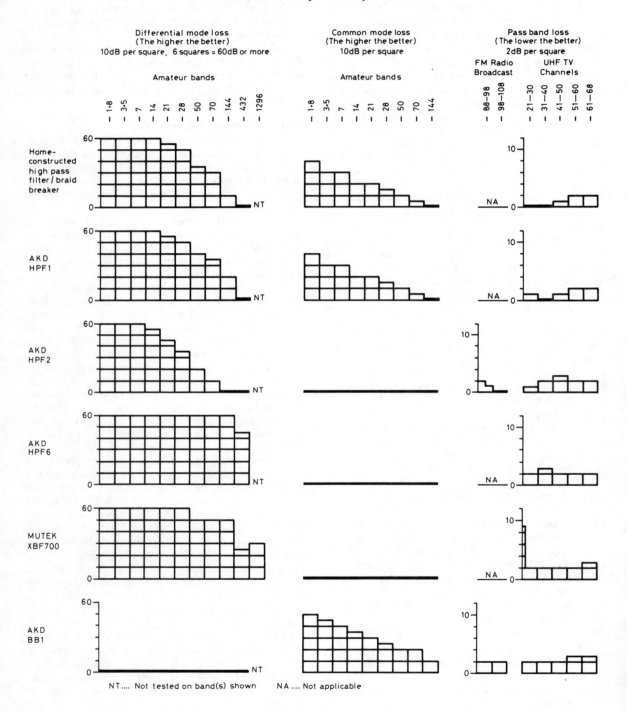

NT.... Not tested on band(s) shown   NA .... Not applicable

Table A3.1 (continued)

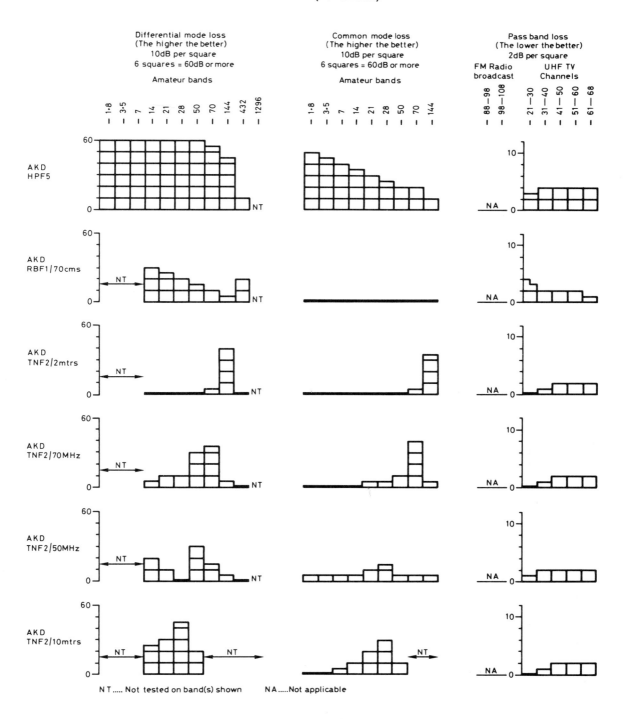

NT ..... Not tested on band(s) shown   NA ..... Not applicable

Table A3.1 (continued)

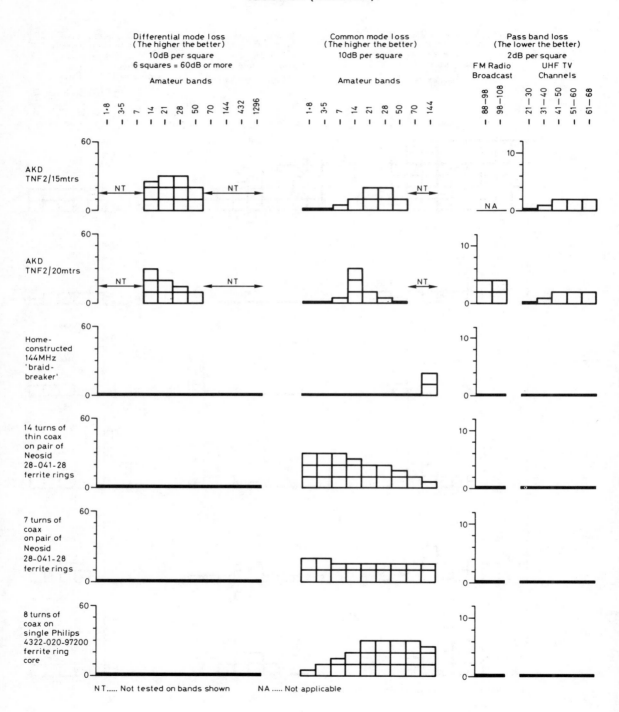

NT..... Not tested on bands shown   NA ..... Not applicable

Table A3.1 (continued)

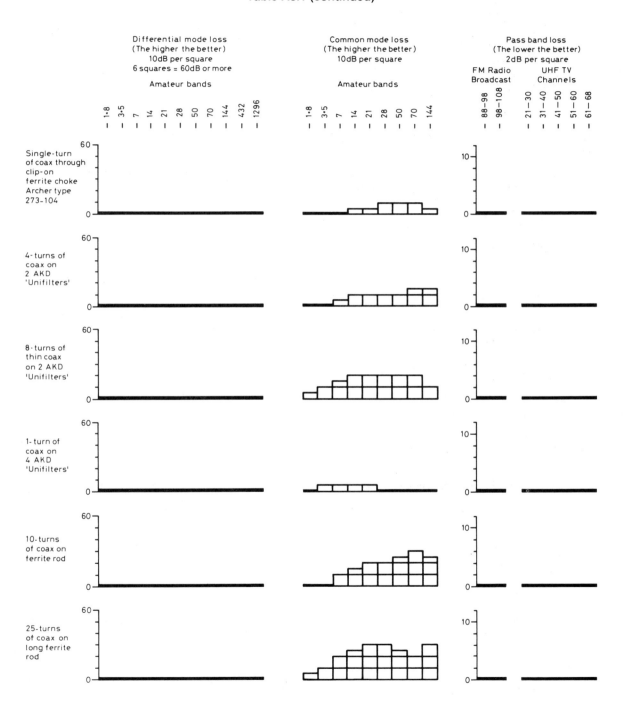

Filter stop-band loss – differential mode

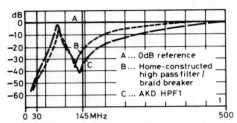

Fig A3.1. Home-constructed high-pass filter/braid-breaker and AKD HPF1, differential mode, grounded source and load, 0–500MHz

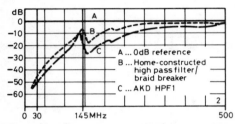

Fig A3.2. Home-constructed high-pass filter/braid-breaker and AKD HPF1, differential mode, 'floating' source, 0–500MHz

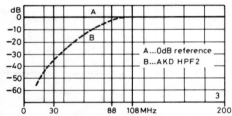

Fig A3.3. AKD HPF2, differential mode, 0–200MHz

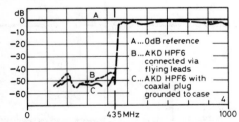

Fig A3.4. AKD HPF6, differential mode, 0–1000MHz

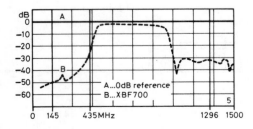

Fig A3.5. Mutek XBF700 stripline filter, differential mode, 0–1500MHz

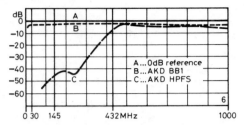

Fig A3.6. AKD BB1 and HPFS, differential mode, 0–1000MHz

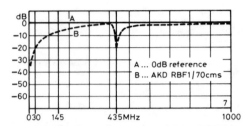

Fig A3.7. AKD RBF1/70cm, differential mode, 0–1000MHz

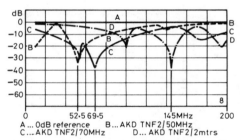

Fig A3.8. AKD TNF2/2m, TNF2/70MHz and TNF2/50MHz, differential mode, 'floating' source, 0–200MHz

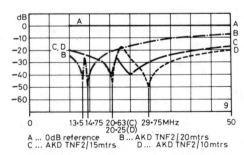

Fig A3.9. AKD TNF2/10m, TNF2/15m and TNF2/20m, differential mode, 'floating' source, 0–50MHz

Filter pass-band loss

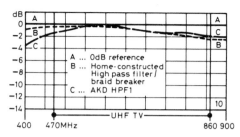

Fig A3.10. Home-constructed high-pass filter/braid-breaker and AKD HPF1, differential mode pass band, 2dB/division, 400–900MHz

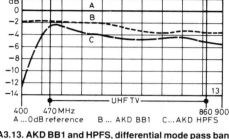

Fig A3.13. AKD BB1 and HPFS, differential mode pass band, 2dB/division, 400–900MHz

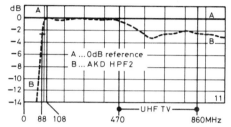

Fig A3.11. AKD HPF2, differential mode pass band, 2dB/division, 0–1000MHz

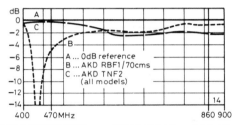

Fig A3.14. AKD RBF1/70cm and AKD TNF2 (all models), differential mode pass band, 2dB/division, 400–900MHz

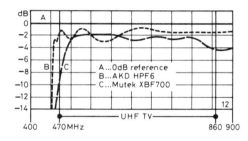

Fig A3.12. AKD HPF6 and Mutek XBF700, differential mode pass band, 2dB/division, 400–900MHz

Filter stop-band loss – common mode

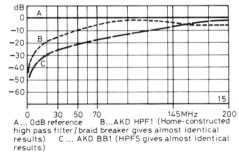

Fig A3.15. Home-constructed high-pass filter/braid-breaker and AKD HPF1, BB1 and HPFS, common mode, 0–200MHz

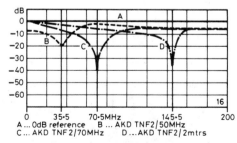

Fig A3.16. AKD TNF2/50MHz, TNF2/70MHz and TNF2/2m, common mode, 0–50MHz

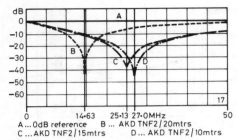

A ... 0dB reference   B ... AKD TNF2/20mtrs
C ... AKD TNF2/15mtrs   D ... AKD TNF2/10mtrs

Fig A3.17. AKD TNF2/20m, TNF2/15m and TNF2/10m, common mode, 0–50MHz

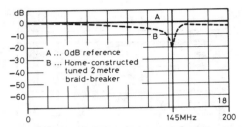

Fig A3.18. Home-constructed tuned 145MHz braid-breaker, common mode, 0–200MHz

Equivalent circuits, appearance etc

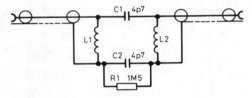

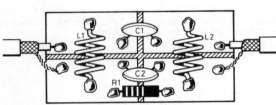

L1 and L2 .... 4-turns of 20swg (0·9mm) wire
6mm i/d x 6mm long

Fig A3.19. Home-constructed high-pass filter and braid-breaker circuit diagram and layout. PCB is single-sided 50 × 25mm. Scrape grooves approx 1.5mm wide in copper to leave four areas as shown. (From the DTI booklet *How to Improve Television and Radio Reception*.)

Fig A3.21. AKD HPF2 equivalent circuit

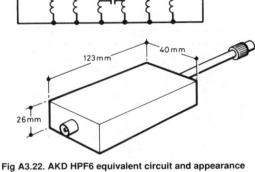

Fig A3.22. AKD HPF6 equivalent circuit and appearance

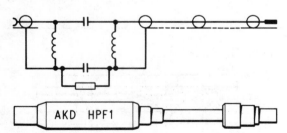

Fig A3.20. AKD HPF1 equivalent circuit and appearance

INPUT/OUTPUT
Ground to
ground-plane
on back of
board

OUTPUT/INPUT
Ground to
ground-plane
on back of
board

Fig A3.23. Mutek XBF700 stripline filter PCB

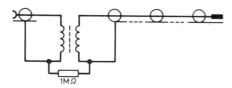

Fig A3.24. AKD BB1 equivalent circuit

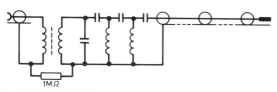

Fig A3.25. AKD HPFS equivalent circuit

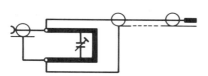

Fig A3.26. AKD RBF1 equivalent circuit

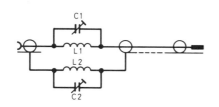

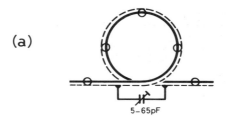

(a)

5–65pF

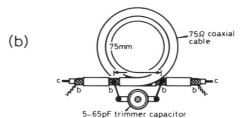

(b)

75mm

75Ω coaxial cable

5–65pF trimmer capacitor

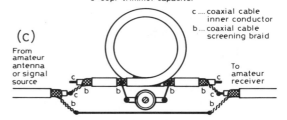

(c)

c .... coaxial cable inner conductor
b .... coaxial cable screening braid

From amateur antenna or signal source

To amateur receiver

Fig A3.28. Home-constructed 144MHz band tuned braid-breaker. (a) Equivalent circuit. (b) Method of construction. (c) Method of tuning

Fig A3.27. AKD TNF2 tuned notch filter range (all models) equivalent circuit

Ferrite chokes – common-mode loss

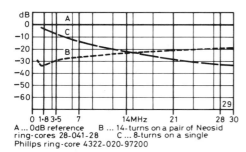

A ... 0dB reference   B ... 14-turns on a pair of Neosid ring-cores 28-041-28   C ... 8-turns on a single Philips ring-core 4322-020-97200

Fig A3.29. Neosid 28-041-28 and Philips 4322-020-97200 ring cores as common-mode chokes, 0–30MHz

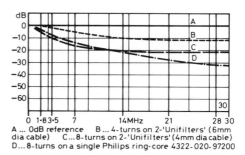

A ... 0dB reference   B ... 4-turns on 2-'Unifilters' (6mm dia cable)   C...8-turns on 2-'Unifilters' (4mm dia cable)
D...8-turns on a single Philips ring-core 4322-020-97200

Fig A3.30. AKD Unifilter clip-on chokes and Philips 4322-020-97200 ring core as common-mode chokes, 0–30MHz

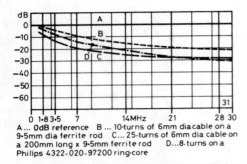

A ... 0dB reference   B ... 10-turns of 6mm dia cable on a
9·5mm dia ferrite rod   C ... 25-turns of 6mm dia cable on
a 200mm long x 9·5mm ferrite rod   D ... 8-turns on a
Philips 4322-020-97200 ring-core

Fig A3.31. Ferrite rod and Philips 4322-020-97200 ring core as common-mode chokes, 0–30MHz

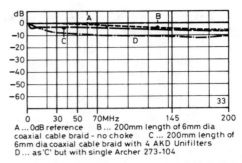

A ... 0dB reference   B ... 200mm length of 6mm dia
coaxial cable braid - no choke   C ... 200mm length of
6mm dia coaxial cable braid with 4 AKD Unifilters
D ... as 'C' but with single Archer 273-104

Fig A3.33. Single-turn clip-on chokes, 0–200MHz, single Archer 273-105 and four AKD Unifilters

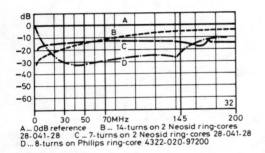

A ... 0dB reference   B ... 14-turns on 2 Neosid ring-cores
28-041-28   C ... 7-turns on 2 Neosid ring-cores 28-041-28
D ... 8-turns on Philips ring-core 4322-020-97200

Fig A3.32. Neosid 28-041-28 and Philips 4322-020-97200 ring cores as common-mode chokes, 0–200MHz

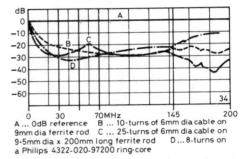

A ... 0dB reference   B ... 10-turns of 6mm dia cable on
9mm dia ferrite rod   C ... 25-turns of 6mm dia cable on
9·5mm dia x 200mm long ferrite rod   D ... 8-turns on
a Philips 4322-020-97200 ring-core

Fig A3.34. Ferrite rod and Philips 4322-020-97200 ring core as common-mode choke, 0–200MHz

Ferrite core details

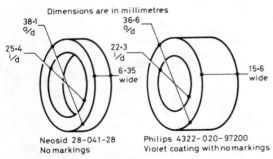

Dimensions are in millimetres

38·1 %/d
25·4 i/d
6·35 wide
Neosid 28-041-28
No markings

36·6 %/d
22·3 i/d
15·6 wide
Philips 4322-020-97200
Violet coating with no markings

Fig A3.35. Ferrite ring dimensions

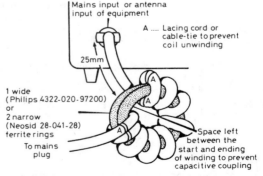

Mains input or antenna input of equipment
A .... Lacing cord or cable-tie to prevent coil unwinding
25mm
1 wide (Philips 4322-020-97200) or 2 narrow (Neosid 28-041-28) ferrite rings
To mains plug
Space left between the start and ending of winding to prevent capacitive coupling

Fig A3.36. Ferrite rings on mains lead or coaxial cable

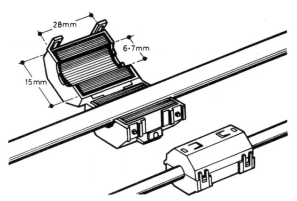

Fig A3.37. Archer 273-105 clip-on ferrite choke dimensions

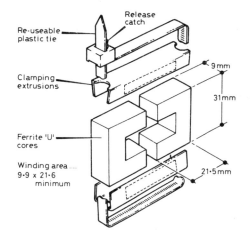

Fig A3.38. AKD Unifilter dimensions

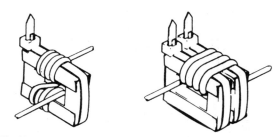

Fig A3.39. Common-mode choke using AKD Unifilters

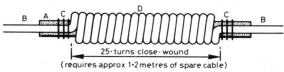

25-turns close-wound

(requires approx 1·2 metres of spare cable)

A .... Ferrite rod, 9·5mm dia   B .... Keep the two ends of the winding
separated especially at VHF   C .... Cable securely bound to ferrite
rod using cable-ties, lacing-cord, etc   D .... Loudspeaker cable,
mains cable, coaxial cable, etc

Fig A3.40. Common-mode choke using ferrite rod

Test methods etc

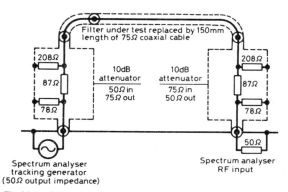

Fig A3.41. Differential-mode 75Ω filter test, grounded source and load, 0dB reference

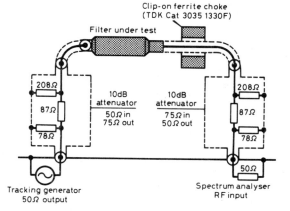

Fig A3.42. Differential-mode 75Ω filter test, grounded source and load, measurement of filter loss

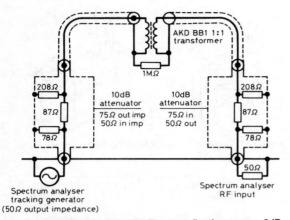

Fig A3.43. Differential-mode 75Ω filter test, floating source, 0dB reference

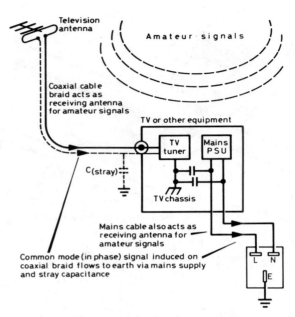

Fig A3.45. Illustration of common-mode signal pick-up

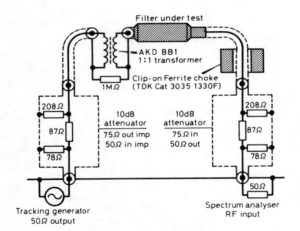

Fig A3.44. Differential-mode 75Ω filter test, floating source, measurement of filter loss

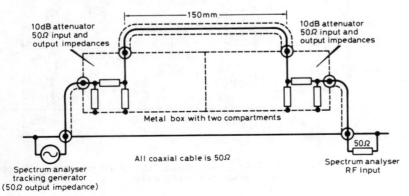

Fig A3.46. Common-mode filter test and ferrite choke test, 0dB reference

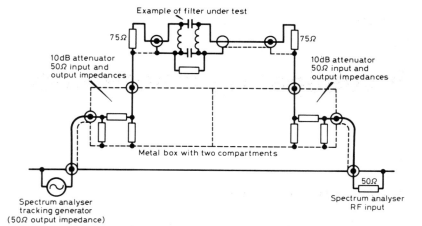

Fig A3.47. Common-mode filter test, measurement of loss in a 50Ω circuit

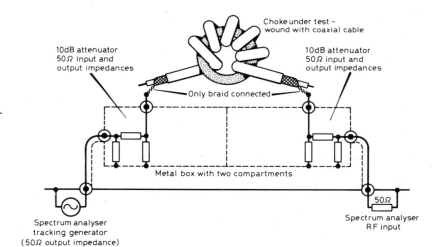

Fig A3.48. Ferrite choke test, measurement of loss in a 50Ω circuit

Investigating interference

Tracking down the interference

Where the source of interference cannot be found by observation, assisted by a little judicious questioning, it will be necessary to resort to more subtle methods.

First check to see how much of the spectrum is affected by the interference and particularly see if it can be received on a medium-wave receiver which is tuned away from any strong broadcast signals. If it can then you are in luck, since almost every household possesses a portable MF receiver with a ferrite-rod antenna. This can be used as a direction finder, using the null to indicate the direction of the interference. There are two nulls, one for each condition where the rod antenna is in line with the signal. The easiest way to resolve the ambiguity is to check the null from several different places. If several helpers with their own receivers are available the task can be made much simpler and has the merit of providing innocent entertainment – particularly to passers-by!

If the interference is limited to the HF bands the simplest approach is to use a portable receiver with a short whip antenna, and try to find where the signal is strongest. In difficult cases it may be necessary to resort to direction finding, but this could involve a lot of experimentation to make a satisfactory loop antenna [1].

Above about 100MHz, a crude but effective technique is to use a 'dipole on a stick'. This can easily be constructed from two lengths of copper rod mounted on a wooden or plastic 'T', as shown in Fig A4.1. A simple

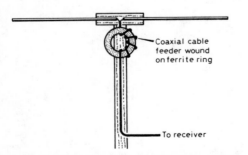

Fig A4.1. The dipole on a stick. A simple balun is formed by winding about seven turns of coaxial cable on a ferrite ring

choke balun can be made by winding a few turns of the coaxial feeder on a ferrite ring, in the same way as for a ferrite choke on a TV feeder. The choke should be as near to the dipole as possible. Minimum signal will be received when the ends of the dipole are pointing towards the source of the interference. Usually incidental interference is a mixture of horizontal and vertical polarisation but, in cases where there is little or no horizontally polarised component direction, indications will be confusing and it is better just to move about with the antenna to find where the signal is maximum, holding the dipole in whichever position gives best results. Generally it is easier to detect changes of signal strength if the receiver is switched to AM or SSB rather than FM, and an S-meter is a great help. Where the source is a radio transmitter some distance away, rather than a local incidental interference source, it may be necessary to turn to proper direction-finding techniques such as are used by VHF DF enthusiasts [1, 2].

Estimating signal strength

This is not an easy matter, and even professionals armed with expensive equipment are wary of the practical accuracy of measurements made in environments which are cluttered by buildings and vegetation. It is most important to keep in mind the difference between the actual accuracy of a reading and the significance of the measurement in terms of the problem under investigation. In most investigations the field strength will vary markedly over quite small distances, as the main and reflected signals add and subtract, or as re-radiation from partially resonant conductors takes place. In practice, the best that the amateur can hope to achieve is to get some idea of the strength of the signal as an aid to problem solving. In particular, do not be tempted to use such measurements to 'lay down the law' to third parties – you could end up with a very red face!

Measurements at VHF

At these frequencies it is often practical to make a portable half-wave dipole and in this case both theory and practice are straightforward.

The signal across a 75Ω load at the centre of a half-wave dipole is:

$$V = E\lambda/2\pi$$

where V is the PD in volts, E is the field strength in volts/metre, and λ is the wavelength in metres.

Connecting the dipole of Fig A4.1 to a receiver with a calibrated S-meter will enable the voltage at the input to be determined. From this the field strength can be found from:

$$E = 2\pi V/\lambda$$

Modern measuring receivers usually have a 50Ω input impedance, and a small correction should be made for this by adding 2dB. If the impedance is doubtful, as it will be with most communication receivers, it can be made to be 50 or 75Ω as required by using an attenuator. A 6dB attenuator would be suitable, and 75Ω devices are available from component suppliers for TV use. The receiver, with attenuator attached, should be calibrated using a signal generator.

In most cases the polarisation of the field will not be known, so the dipole should be turned around both horizontally and vertically until a maximum is found. So far as possible, the dipole should be held away from obstructions and as high up as the circumstances permit. Inevitably reflections will be present, so move around to find an average reading.

Measurements at HF

To make and calibrate an antenna other than a half-wave dipole is no easy matter, and commercial units are very expensive, underlining the difficulty of design and calibration. Fortunately, we are looking for a rough indication rather than an accurate measurement, so that use can be made of a relatively simple method of calculating the relationship between antenna voltage and field strength for electrically short antennas. There is not much information on the practical application of the simple technique described below, and discovering just what can be achieved would be an interesting experimental project.

In discussing the active antenna in Chapter 7, reference was made to the effective series impedance which drops a significant portion of the signal voltage unless the load resistance is very high. If a dipole is shorter than a half-wave then the reactance will be capacitive, and this capacitance is in series with the radiation resistance (Fig A4.2). If the antenna is less than about a quarter-wave long (from end to end – not each element) then the capacitive reactance will be so much larger than the radiation resistance that the latter can be neglected. The reactance will also be large compared to a load resistance of 50 or 75Ω, so that we can forget the complexities of resistance and reactance and assume that the effective

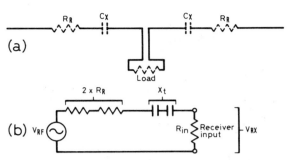

Fig A4.2. (a) The effective resistance and reactance of a short dipole. (b) The equivalent circuit. If $X_t \gg R_R$ and R_{in} then $V_{RX} = V_{RF} \times (R_{in}/X_t)$

loss of signal is simply the ratio of load resistance to antenna reactance.

The reactance can be calculated from:

$$X_c = 2 \times (-j \times 138 (\log l/r) \times \cot G)$$

where l is the length of each element of the antenna (half the overall dipole length); r is the radius of the elements; G is the electrical length of each element.

This is actually much simpler than it appears. In our rough calculation we do not wish to know the phase of the currents, so that we can ignore the '$-j$', and 'cot' is simply the reciprocal of the tangent ($1/\tan$).

Take, for example, a short dipole with element lengths of 50cm and element diameter of 2mm. The frequency will be assumed to be 14MHz ($\lambda = 21.4$m).

$l = 0.5$m; $r = 1$mm so l/r is 500, and log 500 is 2.7.
G is the ratio of l to λ (in this case expressed in degrees). $(0.5/21.4) \times 360 = 8.4°$ and tan 8.4° = 0.148.
cot 8.4 degrees is $1/\tan = 6.77$.

In round figures, for both elements, we get a total $X_c = 2500 \times 2 = 5000\Omega$. For a receiver with a 50Ω input the loss of signal will be approximately 50/5000 or 40dB.

The electric field intercepted by a short dipole is about half its physical length, so that a dipole 1m from end to end and aligned parallel to an electric field of 1V/m will pick up an EMF of 0.5V. This adds another 6dB to our calculation. The total loss from field strength to receiver input would be 46dB. For the 1V/m field, this would give about 5mV at the receiver input.

The effect is as if there were a capacitor in each element of the dipole – about 4.5pF in the above example. This capacitance is really a basic property of the antenna, staying constant with frequency, and depending only on the length and thickness of the elements. There are other ways of calculating this capacitance, and these give roughly the same value [3].

The general construction of the short dipole can be as for the half-wave dipole of Fig A4.1, but for HF frequencies

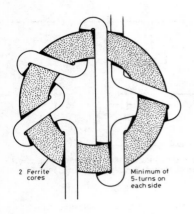

2 Ferrite
cores

Minimum of
5-turns on
each side

Fig A4.3. Choke balun wound to minimise input/output capacitance

the choke balun will require more turns – at least 10 and preferably 14 turns on two rings. The self-capacitance of the choke can be reduced by winding as shown in Fig A4.3. At lower frequencies in the HF band, the difficulties of obtaining sufficient signal with reasonable element lengths, and of achieving reasonable balun performance, will make this technique less attractive.

References

[1] *The ARRL Antenna Book*, 14th edn, ARRL, Chapter 14.
[2] 'VHF direction finding with a miniaturized beam', C J Seymour, *Radio Communication* October 1983.
[3] 'EMC Matters', *Radio Communication* April 1991.

Appendix 5

Useful data

50 AND 75Ω ATTENUATORS

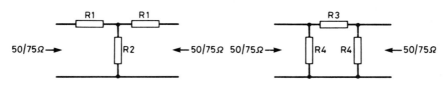

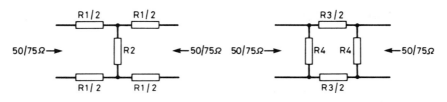

Attenuation (dB)	T pad				π pad			
	50Ω		75Ω		50Ω		75Ω	
	R1	R2	R1	R2	R3	R4	R3	R4
1	2.9	433	4.3	647	5.8	870	8.6	1305
2	5.7	215	8.6	323	11.6	436	17.4	654
3	8.5	142	12.8	213	17.6	292	26.4	439
4	11.3	105	17.0	157	23.8	221	35.8	331
5	14.0	82	21.0	123.4	30.4	179	45.6	268
6	16.6	67	25.0	100	37.3	151	56.0	226
7	19.0	56	28.7	83.8	44.8	131	67.2	196
8	21.5	47	32.3	71	52.3	116	79.3	174
9	23.8	41	35.7	61	61.6	105	92.4	158
10	26.0	35	39.0	52.7	70.7	96	107	144
11	28.0	30.6	42.0	45.9	81.6	89	123	134
12	30.0	26.8	45.0	40.2	93.2	84	140	125
13	31.7	23.5	47.6	35.3	106	78.3	159	118
14	33.3	20.8	50.0	31.2	120	74.9	181	112
15	35.0	18.4	52.4	25.0	136	71.6	204	107
20	41.0	10.0	61.4	15.2	248	61	371	91.5
25	44.7	5.6	67.0	8.5	443	56	666	83.9
30	47.0	3.2	70.4	4.8	790	53.2	1186	79.7
35	48.2	1.8	72.4	2.7	1406	51.8	2108	77.7
40	49.0	1.0	73.6	1.5	2500	51	3750	76.5

UNITED KINGDOM TV CHANNEL FREQUENCIES

BAND IV

Channel	Frequency (MHz)	
	Vision	Sound
21	471.25	477.25
22	479.25	485.25
23	487.25	493.25
24	495.25	501.25
25	503.25	509.25
26	511.25	517.25
27	519.25	525.25
28	527.25	533.25
29	535.25	541.25
30	543.25	549.25
31	551.25	557.25
32	559.25	565.25
33	567.25	573.25
34	575.25	581.25
35	583.25	589.25
36	591.25	597.25
37	599.25	605.25

Channel	Frequency (MHz)	
	Vision	Sound
38	607.25	613.25
39	615.25	621.25
40	623.25	629.25
41	631.25	637.25
42	639.25	645.25
43	647.25	653.25
44	655.25	661.25
45	663.25	669.25
46	671.25	677.25
47	679.25	685.25
48	687.25	693.25
49	695.25	701.25
50	703.25	709.25
51	711.25	717.25
52	719.25	725.25
53	727.25	733.25
54	735.25	741.25

BAND V

Channel	Frequency (MHz)	
	Vision	Sound
55	743.25	749.25
56	751.25	757.25
57	759.25	765.25
58	767.25	773.25
59	775.25	781.25
60	783.25	789.25
61	791.25	797.25
62	799.25	805.25
63	807.25	813.25
64	815.25	821.25
65	823.25	829.25
66	831.25	837.25
67	839.25	845.25
68	847.25	853.25

EMC ASPECTS OF THE AMATEUR BANDS FROM 1810kHz TO 440MHz

The bands quoted are those allocated in the UK.

1810 to 2000kHz
General
This band is shared with the Maritime Mobile Service and is allocated in the UK on the basis that no harmful interference is caused to that service. Breakthrough to cordless telephones on the CT1 system which use frequencies of about 1.7MHz (base transmit, handset receive) is a possibility. Image interference (tuneable breakthrough) to medium-wave broadcast receivers is common.

Harmonics
All harmonics up to the fifteenth fall into the HF band. Harmonics are unlikely to cause any problems in residential areas.

3500 to 3800kHz
General
This band is a shared band by several primary users of which the Amateur Service is one. Direct breakthrough to the video of TV sets and VCR playback amplifiers is fairly common.

Harmonics
All harmonics up to the eighth fall into the HF band. Harmonics are not likely to cause any problems in residential areas.

7000 to 7100kHz
General
This band is allocated exclusively to the Amateur Service on a worldwide basis.

Harmonics
Harmonics could be a problem in regions where VHF TV broadcasting on Band 1 (approximately 47 to 72MHz, depending on location) is still in use. (TV broadcasting in Band 1 has declined over the years and has been discontinued completely in some countries, including the UK.)

10,100 to 10,150kHz
General
This is a shared band. The Amateur Service is the secondary user. Direct breakthrough into the 10.7MHz IF of VHF broadcast receivers is a possibility.

Harmonics
Harmonics could be a problem in regions where VHF TV broadcasting on Band 1 is still in use.

14,000 to 14,350kHz
General
This band is allocated exclusively to the Amateur Service on a worldwide basis.

Harmonics
Harmonics can be a serious problem in regions where VHF TV on Band 1 is still in use. It is possible that the seventh harmonic could cause interference to VHF radio broadcasting on Band 2 (88 to 108MHz).

18,068 to 18,168kHz
General
This band has been allocated to the amateur service, but in practice it will be some time before non-amateur activity ceases.

Harmonics
Harmonics can be a serious problem in regions where VHF TV on Band 1 is still in use. The fifth harmonic falls into the lower part of VHF radio broadcast Band 2 (88 to 108MHz). The second harmonic (36MHz) could cause IF breakthrough to TV receivers.

21,000 to 21,450kHz
General
This band is allocated exclusively to the Amateur Service on a worldwide basis.

Harmonics
Harmonics can be a serious problem in regions where VHF TV on Band 1 is still in use. The fifth harmonic falls in the upper part of VHF radio broadcast Band 2.

24,890 to 24,990kHz
General
This band has been allocated to the Amateur Service, but in practice it will be some time before non-amateur activity ceases.

Harmonics

Harmonics can be a serious problem in regions where VHF TV on Band 1 is still in use. The fourth harmonic falls in the VHF radio broadcast Band 2. The second harmonic could cause problems to low-power control and communication devices operating on frequencies around 49MHz.

28,000 to 29,700MHz
General

This band is allocated exclusively to the Amateur Service on a worldwide basis. Some low-power control devices such as radio door chimes etc operate on specific frequencies in the CEPT Citizens Band (26.96 to 27.4MHz). Breakthrough to such devices is a possibility.

Harmonics

Harmonics can be a serious problem in regions where VHF TV on Band 1 is still in use. The third harmonic of frequencies above 29.3MHz will fall into VHF radio broadcast Band 2.

50.0 to 52.0MHz
General

This band has become available in the UK since the closing of VHF TV broadcasting. In some locations, care may be needed to avoid interference to TV in other countries. Breakthrough to CT1 cordless telephones operating near 47.5MHz, or to low-power control and communication devices operating on frequencies around 49MHz is a possibility.

Harmonics

The second harmonic falls into the upper end of VHF radio broadcast Band 2. Third harmonics could cause interference to mobile and other services operating between 150 and 156MHz. Radio astronomy uses frequencies between in the lower section of this band (up to 153MHz).

70.0 to 70.50MHz
General

This is not an internationally allocated band. Available to amateurs in the UK on a secondary basis.

Harmonics

The second harmonic (140 to 141MHz) falls into a band used by various services depending on region. Includes aircraft, land mobile and space research. The third harmonic (210 to 211.5MHz) falls into the VHF TV Band 3, which is no longer used for TV broadcasting in the UK. Other services such as mobile communications will operate in this band.

144 to 146MHz
General

This band is allocated exclusively to the Amateur Service on a worldwide basis.

Harmonics

The second harmonic (288 to 292MHz) falls into a band allocated for fixed and mobile operation, the specific use depending on the region and country. The third harmonic falls into the 430 to 440MHz amateur band. The fourth harmonic (576 to 584MHz) could cause a problem to UHF TV (Band 4, channels 34 and 35 in the UK). The fifth harmonic (720 to 730MHz) could cause interference to UHF TV (Band 5, channels 52 and 53 in the UK).

430 to 440MHz
General

In the UK this band is allocated to the Amateur Service on a secondary basis. There are also some special restrictions in certain locations. The lower end of UHF TV Band 4 is not far above this band, so that breakthrough via TV antenna and normal receiving path is a likely possibility.

Harmonics

The second harmonic (860 to 880MHz) falls above the UK UHF Band 5 TV band, but other countries use frequencies above 860MHz for broadcasting and in such cases second-harmonic interference to TV is likely. The third harmonic (1290 to 1320MHz) falls into the 1240 to 1325MHz amateur band but, since this band is shared by other services, third-harmonic interference to non-amateur services is possible. Third-harmonic breakthrough into the first IF of a satellite TV receivers is possible but not likely.

TECHNICAL TERMS AND ABBREVIATIONS

The meanings given are those normally used in informal technical discussion.

Aerial
Same as 'antenna'. Widely used in the UK in relation to domestic radio and TV etc. ('Antenna' is used for most engineering purposes.)

Antenna
A radiator or collector of electromagnetic energy.

AMU
Antenna matching unit. Same as ATU.

ATU
Antenna (or aerial) tuning unit. Device to tune out the reactance of an antenna, and match the radiation resistance to the load or source – usually 50Ω.

Balun
Balance-to-unbalance transformer. Often used to connect an unbalanced (coaxial) feeder to a balanced antenna.

BCI
Interference to broadcast radio reception.

Beryllia
Beryllium oxide. A white ceramic used in power transistors etc. Very toxic when in the form of fine particles.

Breakthrough
Used (particularly by radio amateurs) to describe interference caused by the legitimate radiation from a transmitter entering a piece of equipment which has insufficient immunity.

Bond
To connect together by a low-impedance path.

Braid
The woven outer conductor of coaxial cables. The woven screen around screened cables. A woven (flat) conductor which gives a large conductor area and hence a low inductance.

Characteristic impedance
The resistive impedance presented to an RF signal by an infinitely long transmission line or by a transmission line terminated in a resistance equal to the characteristic impedance.

Choke
An inductor used to restrict the flow of AC.

Common-mode currents
Currents flowing in one direction on two or more conductors, in contrast to the go-and-return differential signals.

Counterpoise
A wire suspended some distance above the ground, insulated from earth, and connected to an antenna system in place of a true earth.

Earth (radio)
A conductor buried in the ground. Assumed to be at zero potential for radio frequencies.

Earth (mains)
The protective conductor (at nominal earth potential).

EMC
Electromagnetic compatibility. The ability of electronic devices and systems to operate without mutual interference.

EMI
Electromagnetic interference.

EMP
Electromagnetic pulse. A large pulse of electromagnetic energy caused by lightning or nuclear explosion.

Far field
The field at a distance, where the energy is no longer affected by the antenna. The electric and magnetic fields are at right-angles to one another, and to the direction of propagation.

Feedthrough capacitor
A capacitor which mounts directly onto a screen and has a lead passing through it.

Feeder
A transmission line used to transfer the power from a transmitter or ATU to the antenna. Usually a coaxial cable or open-wire line.

Ferrite
Magnetic material which can be manufactured with a wide range of properties. Usually it has a high electrical resistance.

Filter
A circuit which allows some frequencies to pass with a small loss, while attenuating other frequencies.

Ground (radio)
Same as earth.

Ground (signal)
The path by which an unbalanced signal returns to its source.

Ground (system)
Zero potential to which other potentials are referred. Chassis potential.

Ground, clean
A ground connection reserved for small-signal operation. (Separate from the main ground).

Ground plane (of a circuit)
A large area of copper comprising all or most of one side of a PCB. Effectively connects together points of nominal zero potential by a low-impedance path. The 0V power supply rail is usually connected to the ground plane.

Harmonic
A spurious emission harmonically related to the carrier.

Image interference
Interference caused by an unwanted signal, which is on the opposite side of the local oscillator to the wanted signal, beating with the local oscillator to give the IF.

Intermods
Short for 'intermodulation products'. Outputs (usually unwanted) caused by two or more signals mixing in a non-linear circuit.

Instability
Unwanted oscillation, or a tendency to oscillate.

Mains
The domestic electricity supply.

Near field
The field relatively close to an antenna, where energy is exchanged between the field and the antenna. The relationship between the electric and magnetic fields is complex.

Parasitic oscillations
An unwanted oscillation involving circuit conditions incidental to the main design aims.

Pass band
The band of frequencies passed by a filter with small loss.

PCB
Printed circuit board.

PCB
Polychlorinated biphenyls. (Oil used at one time in certain types of transformers and capacitors etc. Highly toxic; can be absorbed through the skin.)

PIPs
Passive intermodulation products. Intermods caused by corroded contacts in passive metalwork such as masts and gutters. Sometimes called 'rusty bolt effect'.

PME
Protective multiple earthing (see Appendix 1).

PMR
Private mobile radio. Radio communication for business purposes.

Polarisation (of radio wave)
The direction of the electric field. May be linear (eg horizontal or vertical), circular (rotating) or elliptical (a combination of linear and circular).

Primary user
This is an official definition. So far as amateurs are concerned, it is the service which has the 'right of way' on a shared band.

Protected service
So far as amateurs are concerned, this means a service which can expect official action to be taken against sources of interference. Amateur radio is not a protected service.

Radiation resistance
A fictitious resistance which would dissipate the same power as that radiated by a particular antenna when transmitting, or would be the source resistance when receiving.

Radiation field
Same as 'far field'.

Rail
A power supply line, eg +5V rail; −12V rail; 0V rail etc.

RFI
Radio-frequency interference.

Screen
Conductive enclosure or partition. Sometimes used instead of 'braid' to describe a woven outer conductor.

Secondary user
This is an official definition. So far as amateurs are concerned, it is the service which does not have 'right of way'. On a shared band, where the Amateur Service is a secondary user, amateurs must not cause interference to the primary user.

Second-channel interference
An old name for image interference.

Selectivity
The ability to reject unwanted, off tune signals while receiving the wanted one.

Shield
Same as screen.

Splatter
Spurious emissions relatively close to the nominal carrier frequency. Caused by non-linearity (often due to overdriving) in an SSB transmitter.

Spurious
Short for 'spurious emission'. Any radiation outside the normal bandwidth of the transmission.

Stop band
Frequencies which are attenuated by a filter. Frequencies outside the pass band.

Transmatch
Same as ATU.

Transmission line
Conductors arranged to convey RF energy between different parts of an installation. Usually coaxial cable or open-wire line.

TVI
Interference to TV reception.

VCR
Video cassette recorder.

White noise
Noise which can be resolved into a continuous spectrum of component frequencies. The power in equal bandwidths at any part of the spectrum is the same. Called 'white' by analogy with white light which contains all colours.

0V (rail)
Zero potential to which other potentials are referred. Normally the 0V terminal of the power supply is connected to this rail. Often used interchangeably with 'ground'.

Index

Some other RSGB publications...

❏ AMATEUR RADIO TECHNIQUES

Basically an ideas and source book, this ever-popular work brings together a large selection of novel antennas, circuits and devices, together with many fault-finding and constructional hints.

❏ HF ANTENNA COLLECTION

An invaluable compendium of outstanding articles and short pieces which were published in *Radio Communication* during 1968 to 1989. As well as ingenious designs for single-element, beam and miniature antennas, there is a wealth of information on ancillary topics such as feeders, tuners, baluns, testing, modelling, and the mechanics of mounting an antenna safely.

❏ PACKET RADIO PRIMER

A light-hearted introduction to the exciting new world of packet radio which will help any beginner to get started with the minimum of fuss. Detailed practical advice on connecting up equipment is followed by a guide through the maze of configurations possible. Then sample logs of contacts with the various forms of 'mailbox' are featured to help you get the best out of the network. Much reference information is also included to supplement your equipment manuals.

❏ RSGB AMATEUR RADIO CALL BOOK

As well as a list of all UK and Republic of Ireland radio amateurs, this essential reference work also includes an information directory giving useful addresses, EMC advice, lists of amateur radio clubs, operating data, and much more.

❏ SPACE RADIO HANDBOOK

Space exploration by radio is exciting and it is open to anyone! This book shows you how it is done, and the equipment you will need. It covers the whole field of space radio communication and experimentation, including meteor scatter, moonbounce, satellites and simple radio astronomy. A particularly valuable feature is a collection of experiments which will be of interest to schools wishing to explore the many educational possibilities. If you are ready to use radio to explore beyond the atmosphere, let this book be your guide.

❏ VHF/UHF MANUAL

This standard UK textbook on the theory and practice of amateur radio reception and transmission at VHF and UHF includes full constructional details of many items of equipment. While the contents are intended primarily for the amateur radio enthusiast, there is much information of value to the professional engineer.

 RADIO SOCIETY OF GREAT BRITAIN
Lambda House, Cranborne Road,
Potters Bar, Herts EN6 3JE

RSGB – *representing amateur radio …*
… representing you!

Radio Communication

A magazine which covers a wide range of interests and which features the best and latest amateur radio news. The Society's journal has acquired a world-wide reputation for its content. It strives to maintain its reputation as the best available and is now circulated, free of charge, to members in over 150 countries.

The regular columns in the magazine cater for HF, VHF/UHF, microwaves, SWL, clubs, satellites, data and contests. In addition to technical articles, the highly regarded 'Technical Topics' feature caters for those wishing to keep themselves briefed on recent developments in technical matters. There is also a special column for Novice licensees.

The 'Last Word' is a lively feature in which members can put forward their views and opinions and be sure of receiving a wide audience. To keep members in touch with what's going on in the hobby, events diaries are published each month.

Subsidised advertisements for the equipment you wish to sell can be placed in the magazine, with the advantages of short deadlines and large circulation.

QSL Bureau

Members enjoy the use of the QSL Bureau free of charge for both outgoing and incoming cards. This can save you a good deal of postage.

Special Event Callsigns

Special Event Callsigns in the GB series are handled by RSGB. They give amateurs special facilities for displaying amateur radio to the general public.

Specialised News Sheets

The Society publishes the weekly *DX News-sheet* for HF enthusiasts and the *Microwave Newsletter* for those operating above 1GHz.

Specialised Equipment Insurance

Insurance for your valuable equipment which has been arranged specially for members. The rates are very advantageous.

Audio Visual Library

Films, audio and video tapes are available through one of the Society's Honorary Officers for all affiliated groups and clubs.

Reciprocal Licensing Information

Details are available for most countries on the RSGB computer database.

Government Liaison

One of the most vital features of the work of the RSGB is the ongoing liaison with the UK Licensing Authority – presently the Radiocommunications Agency of the Department of Trade and Industry. Setting and maintaining the proper framework in which amateur radio can thrive and develop is essential to the well-being of amateur radio. The Society spares no effort in defence of amateur radio's most precious assets – the amateur bands.

Beacons and Repeaters

The RSGB supports financially all repeaters and beacons which are looked after by the appropriate committee of the Society, ie, 1.8-30MHz by the HF Committee, 30-1000MHz (1GHz) by the VHF Committee and frequencies above 1GHz by the Microwave Committee. For repeaters, the Society's Repeater Management Group has played a major role. Society books such as the *Amateur Radio Call Book* give further details, and computer-based lists giving up-to-date operational status can be obtained by post from HQ.

Operating Awards

A wide range of operating awards are available via the responsible officers: their names can be found in the front pages of *Radio Communication* and in the Society's *Amateur Radio Call Book*. The RSGB also publishes a book which gives details of most major awards.

Contests (HF/VHF/Microwave)

The Society has two contest committees which carry out all work associated with the running of contests. The HF Contests Committee deals with contests below 30MHz, whilst events on frequencies above 30MHz are dealt with by the VHF Contests Committee.

Morse Testing

In April 1986 the Society took over responsibility for morse testing of radio amateurs in the UK. If you wish to take a morse test, write direct to RSGB HQ (Morse tests) for an application form.

Slow Morse

Many volunteers all over the country give up their time to send slow morse over the air to those who are preparing for the 5 and 12 words per minute morse tests. The Society also produces morse instruction tapes.

RSGB Books

The Society publishes a range of books for the radio amateur and imports many others. RSGB members are entitled to a discount on all books purchased from the Society. This discount can offset the cost of membership.

Propagation

The Society's Propagation Studies Committee is highly respected – both within the amateur community and professionally – for its work. Predictions are given in the weekly GB2RS news bulletins and the Society's monthly magazine *Radio Communication*.

Technical and EMC Advice

Although the role of the Society's Technical and Publications Advisory Committee is largely to vet material intended for publication, its members and HQ staff are always willing to help with any technical matters.

Breakthrough in domestic entertainment equipment can be a difficult problem to solve as well as having licensing implications. The Society's EMC Committee is able to offer practical assistance in many cases. The Society also publishes a special book to assist you. Additional advice can be obtained from the EMC Committee Chairman via RSGB HQ.

Planning Permission

There is a special booklet and expert help available to members seeking assistance with planning matters.

GB2RS

A special radio news bulletin transmitted each week and aimed especially at the UK radio amateur and short wave listener. The script is prepared each week by the Society's HQ staff. The transmission schedule for GB2RS is printed regularly in *Radio Communication*, or it can be obtained via the Membership Services Department at HQ. It also appears in the *Amateur Radio Call Book*. The GB2RS bulletin is also sent out over the packet radio network.

Raynet (Radio Amateur Emergency Network)

Several thousand radio amateurs give up their free time to help with local, national and sometimes international emergencies. There is also ample opportunity to practise communication and liaison skills at non-emergency events, such as county shows and charity walks, as a service to the people. For more information or full details of how to join, contact the Membership Services Department at RSGB HQ.

RSGB Exhibitions and Mobile Rallies

The Society's Exhibition and Rally Committee organizes an annual exhibition and an annual mobile rally. Full details and rally calendar can be found in *Radio Communication*.

RSGB Conventions

The Society's diary in *Radio Communication* contains details of all special conventions which are open to all radio amateurs. The Society holds several major conventions each year.

Observation Service

A number of leading national radio societies have volunteers who monitor the amateur bands as a service to the amateur community. Their task is to spot licence infringements and defective transmissions, and report them in a friendly way to the originating station.

Intruder Watch

This helps to protect the exclusive amateur bands by monitoring for stations not authorised to use them.

Send for our Membership Information Pack today and discover how you too can benefit from these services. Write to:

RADIO SOCIETY OF GREAT BRITAIN, Lambda House, Cranborne Road, Potters Bar, Herts EN6 3JE

Notes

THE RADIO AMATEUR'S GUIDE TO EMC (1st edn)

We hope you found this book interesting and useful. Please let us have your comments and suggestions for the next edition so we can make it even better!

CUT ALONG DOTTED LINE

Name... Callsign....................................

Address...

....

....

....

FOLD 1

AFFIX
STAMP
HERE

RSGB Book Editor
Radio Society of Great Britain
Lambda House
Cranborne Road
POTTERS BAR
Herts EN6 3JE

FOLD 2